Juanie
June
1984

THE RAINBOW BOX

THE RAINBOW BOX

BARBARA TURNER SACHS

CONGDON & WEED, INC.
NEW YORK

Library of Congress Cataloging in Publication Data

Sachs, Barbara Turner.
The rainbow box.

I. Title.
PS3569.A228R3 1984 813'.54 83-19017
ISBN 0-86553-102-1
ISBN 0-312-92715-0 (St. Martin's Press)

Published by Congdon & Weed, Inc.
298 Fifth Avenue, New York, N.Y. 10001
Distributed by St. Martin's Press
175 Fifth Avenue, New York, N.Y. 10010
Published simultaneously in Canada by Methuen Publications
2330 Midland Avenue, Agincourt, Ontario M1S 1P7

Printed in the United States of America
Text design by Irving Perkins; display design by Krystyna Skalski
First Edition

To Jon, Jeff, and Jason, who have suspended portions of their childhood for me

PART ONE

Chapter 1

■ IT WAS OCTOBER OF 1920, at an exclusive Connecticut boarding school named the Grove. The place was rich with healthy trees, and staffed with teachers who promised that the boys within the white wooden cottages—all of whom had educational handicaps, emotional problems, nervous disorders, and physical limitations—would bear the fruits of intelligent and gentle care.

In front of a cottage was a brand-new, custom-designed Stutz Bearcat, Excelsior Model SGV, a limited edition, a car so able to reflect the evening moon that it shone more vividly on the hood than in the sky.

From the doors of the cottage slipped a group of young men, out on a spree, good-natured, ass-slapping, sharing a hip flask as they stuffed themselves into the Stutz and peeled out of the premises.

The car slid onto the highway and rode through small towns (not suburbs but towns complete within themselves like slipknots on a sailor's rope) until it was in a wooded section, on a road near the sea.

Edward "Wyck" Hanover had just bought this Stutz. It

was his first car, and there had never been anything like it in his life or in the lives of his friends, Carl and Bobby. It had a three-speed transmission and an air-cooled engine and hydraulic brakes, and besides the 2,400 moving parts on the standard model, he had ordered a bunch of special extras like a cowl ventilator and automatic windshield cleaners. All of which, thank God, broke down or had to be replaced, which gave them a reason to open the hood and finger the owner's manual and consult the supply dealer (not by phone, but by car).

They were possessed by it. Obsessed by it. They chased chickens on back roads and honked through residential sections at midnight and coasted down hills braking at the very last minute on one-lane roads. They gave up meals to run any dimwit errand and went to third-string football games and rustic-boob-sap parties just to show off the car. Criminy. Crispus. They had acceleratoritis, these highway jockeys, sporting two spares on the rear rack because they popped so many pneumatic tires in a week.

The car coughed. Sputtered. Came to a complete stop.

"Feed it some rum."

"This car only moves in a breeze."

Mock grumbling and false aggravation were in this talk, negative bragging and thin frustration that hid a sense of great relief—Oh my God, oh boy, this car needs me, without me it's a wheelchair—for they were all of them car-crazy.

Carl Kretzer, driving, pulled on the No-Back device so the car would not slip down the hill, and jumped out as a rain began. He was visibly older than the other two. Thirty-one, gutty, worldly, an electrician at the school who left his wife at home to do his part of the Roaring

Twenties. A self-appointed guide along life's highway, he showed them how to get three beers for the price of two, and how to flirt with girls, but most of the time Carl told them just to sit quiet and observe, time would come when they could try it for themselves. Practice, Carl said, was just for suckers.

Wyck slid into the driver's seat. He let others tinker with his car, but never take it (love me, love my car, or rather, love my car, love me, useful for keeping friends if you were shy). Wyck was eighteen, tall, elegant, his baby face hidden behind balloon tire glasses. He had paid extra for this engine but was accustomed to things not working, being obstinate, slipping out of his reach. His mother died when he was nine, his father never taught him how to handle small frustrations. He had learned to back off, to wait, to seek the help of others. And, because he was a boy of extraordinary wealth, someone had always stepped in.

Edward Wyck Hanover was a descendant of the pure and populous Hanover line that planted their Protestant family tree in Europe (marriages arranged like international treaties by cartologists, clergy, economists, and assassins). Forced by Catholics then converting and/or killing, they fled to this New World in 1686. Hanover carriages pounded American paths to roads, traded its forests for its farms, dominated its waterways, financed its railroads, created its cities, then named its streets, museums, and phone exchanges. Unerring, strict souls all, they believed in Hell and a punishing God, and were not reticent to do His work on earth. Here were visible, exalted people, as near to perfect as God permits, with few exceptions; one, however, was Edward Wyck.

Wyck had weak eyes, and an early shyness mistaken by his relatives for slowness of the mind. Society has its favorite infirmities, as ice cream has its classic flavors, and learning problems in 1920 were not in vogue. Physical flaws showed perhaps the line was slipping, intelligence after all was clearly inherited and so were mental states.

He was schooled at home until his mother died, her death began a whole new childhood. He had lost his shield, his buffer, his apologist, so off he went, at the age of ten, to be among "his own."

Wyck's schools bordered on being institutions, the medical staff far outnumbering the teachers. Faculty were on "teams," debating hygiene, diet, mental health, as well as education. His sorrow at his mother's death packed up among his things, he carried it from place to place and lived with youths who went home only on major holidays.

Wyck's teachers at the Grove School were paid parents, substitute families, who wrote letters instead of cards at Christmas to mothers and fathers, told them what they wanted to hear and seldom informed on teenagers who slept with baby blankets or kept their pee in bottles. Intelligence, here, ran quite a range, some were slow but there were geniuses among them (high intellect and originality coined as maladjustment). Some were victims of tuberculosis, polio, or asthma, the common thread the money that kept them there, a fidgety lot, all of them turtles created by God without a shell.

Wyck passed the Napier flask to Bobby Melba, the third in the Stutz, a chubby boy who looked as though he took frequent doses of belladonna. Bobby, still choosing to make X's for his name, was clearly conversant in baseball and had no trouble reading comic books but liked to say dirty words and light his hair on fire just to get attention from the cottage master.

Bobby passed the flask to Carl, who took a swig, then seized the crank, making several unsuccessful revolutions in the night. Wyck watched what Carl was doing, then noticed a girl across the street. She was plump. Modern. Around eighteen.

Her name was Faye James, and she stood under an umbrella, an orange cloche pulled over her ears, which made her easily visible in the night. She was singing a dance tune and moving up the street, making a swimming motion with her hands.

Carl spotted her, too. He hurried up his revolutions and he hollered, "Hey, you want a ride?" With that the engine sparked to life.

Faye pretended to ignore them, but her singing became a whisper and her dancing a scuff.

"Hey, you want a lift?" Carl yelled again. He leaped onto the trembling running board and commanded Wyck to swing the car into a big U-turn ending up directly in front of Faye.

"Where are you going?" asked Bobby, pushing open the door.

"To Felham," said Faye, eyeing the car and the boys. "How many of you is there?"

"Just three of us," said Carl. "Look, it's raining and the bus might be stuck."

"Well, I don't know," said Faye.

"We saw one stuck right on the road. I bet it was yours," said Carl.

"Well," said Faye. "I don't know . . . but if you promise not to get squirrely, I'll get in."

▪

THE WOODEN STAIRS ALMOST gave way under her excitement as Faye climbed them two by two to her sister's room. Mary James was posing in front of her full-length mirror, coal-black hair falling in waves down her face, her eyes a lacquer brown. She was olive-skinned, with a slim, rippling body, restless hands, long, liquid legs, and half-undressed feet. Her skirt fell from her hips like a loose trapeze, and she was always moving, though there was nothing anxious or wasted in her movements. They were studied and graceful, and her body was anchored like a plumb line to give it gravity.

She smelled of perfumes used only by the dropper and shone with lotions known by exquisite beauties, and she added silver to her rouge and lined her eyes with three kohl powders and spent hours at a dressing table, yet appeared as natural in her beauty as a private garden in a moist and fertile zone.

Faye collapsed on the bed. "I just met a carful of sheiks, rich sheiks what is loaded."

Mary masked her curiosity from her sister—the more she asked, the less she'd hear. "Oh well, there are lots of sheiks around here."

"I got in their car and . . ." said Faye.

"You took a lift?"

"Yes, I did."

"But you could get killed."

"Oh, they's so rich they don't have to do anything bad."

"Mom and Dad would kill you."

"They won't know. Oh, don't tell, Mary, don't tell. Those sheiks want to go out tomorrow."

"They do?" asked Mary.

"Yes, this one Carl, and another, Edward Wyck," said Faye.

▪

WYCK WAS IN THE school gymnasium, playing one-on-one with an aggressive boy who aimed at his gut when he passed the ball. Wyck excused himself and left the floor.

It had been their plan to meet some hours later to see the girl in the orange hat who said she had a sister.

"My wife asked my brother-in-law to dinner, so I can't wheel into Felham," said Carl.

Bobby sauntered up and giggled. "The girls will mourn for months."

"You can't miss what you can't imagine," said Carl with an obscene wiggle of his hips.

"I . . . I can't go alone," said Wyck.

"Sure you can," said Carl.

"Bbb . . . Bobby?"

"I've got Composition. Go alone. What are you afraid of?"

"I . . . I'm not afraid."

"He's not afraid," said Carl, sticking up for Wyck. "Sure, the girls may get suicidal because I'm not there, but Wyck can handle women." He gave an exaggerated wink to Bobby. "He's a ladies' man at heart."

Bobby giggled hilariously. Wyck started to get angry but checked it. Anger was something he had learned to stay away from. He hated confrontations. Anyway, the giggling boy was right. He'd mess it up somehow.

Carl went on, bragging on behalf of Wyck. "The kid's had a chance to watch a pro. All he has to do is act like me."

"A sawbuck says he won't go," said Bobby.

"A sawbuck says he'll come back with another date for him and me," said Carl.

▪

THAT AFTERNOON, MARY AND Faye slowly strolled up the street, reading a tabloid and trying to seem cool as a breeze.

The Stutz came up the road like a great upholstered sea gull. "That's no struggle-buggy," Faye said to Mary.

Edward Wyck Hanover got out of the car. He walked over to the girls and said, "Ccc . . . Carl told me to tell you, hhh . . . he's sorry but he can't make it."

He stuttered. He stammered.

He has air between his ears, thought Faye.

Mary's heart moved at his difficulty, and she liked the way he looked. He carried his head like a nimbus, and his neck was like a tree.

Faye tried not to look glum. (They went to sunday school. They lived in a good house across from the ocean. They had lots of boys after them, and they were not des-per-ate. But these boys sure were something swell.) "I wasn't expecting him no-how," she said.

"Well, goodbye," he said. "It's nice to meet you. I only ccc . . . came to give you Carl's message. I have to go because . . ." He let the sentence trail into the air, not really wanting to come up with a reason to leave.

"You sheiks is all the same," said Mary. Her mouth was like a pulse.

Wyck's eyes caught on Mary. Her beauty so intense it went into an ache. He turned from it to Faye. "Not me," he said to her, "I'm different."

"If you so different," said Faye, "you can pay for our movie." She jumped into the front and pointed Mary to the back.

Mary sank into leather the color of fresh cream, unthinkable luxury, she felt like something tight within a purse, a piece of jewelry in a custom case. "Sort of thrilling, ain't it?"

They drove to Proctor's movie house in New Rochelle. Proctor's had cut velvet on the seats, a mural of a Turkish harem on the walls, and a pianist playing crashing chords and loud arpeggios as the hero and heroine battled their way up Colorado Falls.

The movie was crowded because of a new show. Faye got to sit next to him, and Mary was separated by two rows, but she could see them. She could see him trying to make some headway with her sister, who slumped into her chair for the first part of the movie. Then something seemed to change her attitude. Mary could see it by Faye's body, for suddenly they were getting very chummy and she was snuggling closer.

Faye looked like a squab, thought Mary, and her eyes are like those beads in dead animal furs, made up to look happy. She's only interested in him because he looks like a real high-flyer. I'm interested in him because I like him, it's not the money, I can work (he has lovelocks like a baby angel, he has manners, he has class). I'd never go after anyone for money. She couldn't concentrate on the movie now, and her sister and Wyck had totally disappeared from sight. She played with the fringe she had crocheted on her bag and strained to look and craned her neck and blocked the view of the child in back of her.

Finally, she saw Faye emerge like a diver coming up from deep water, her hand appearing first, above the seats, waving at Mary, who saw something twinkling in the lantern projector of the movie, it was on her finger, his diamond and sapphire ring flashing out a Morse code of look-at-me.

▪

THE JAMES PARLOR WAS old-fashioned for the twenties, her mother had filled it with a lot of bric-a-brac, a Victrola in one corner, a piano in another, a small table filled with baskets and ornaments, a center table and several chairs, not leaving much space for the inhabitants, which that evening, three nights after the movie, included Faye and Mary and Wyck and Carl.

They were crowded around the piano, Faye was chopping away at "Whispering," and they were sipping fruit punch, taking turns soloing the bridge.

I know it's true
There's no one, dear, but you.

Carl put his hand on Mary's waist. She slipped away, her glance was cold, a telegram of ice. Carl was very forward, very handsy. He was an older man and crass, a real bull-fiddler. Why did Wyck want to pal around with him?

Faye was oozing over Wyck, putting on all kinds of airs.

It wasn't fair that Faye had met Wyck first. Faye was going with Footsie Fuller. Now she was ready to drop him flat, as changeable as hose. Wyck's a Barrymoron, real goon-soup, Faye had said to Mary, not sophisticated or slick like Footsie. But even so, she held Wyck's hand possessively. All his money ree-eeked of wild adventure.

Carl caught Mary's hand and put his head next to hers as he harmonized.

Whis-per-ing why you'll never leave me.
Whis-per-ing why you'll never grieve me.
Whis-per-ing why I love you.

Carl's voice was loud, emphatic, Faye's voice was peppy, Wyck's was matter-of-fact, but Mary's voice outshone them all. She colored notes and braided them like rainbow-painted streamers around a maypole.

Wyck thought Mary was the most beautiful woman he had ever seen. Her tropicality. Her grace. Her eyes. Her nose. He did an inventory, and nothing came up wanting. And there he was with Faye. Carl had paid him the sawbuck, won it back at poker, then come to take Mary out. Wyck would give one hundred sawbucks if Carl would take his hands off her.

Wyck stole hidden glances at Mary and fantasized taking pictures of her with a secret camera, like a reporter getting an illicit shot of a celebrity. He wanted to steal her school yearbook for the picture of her in it. He glanced around the room for the family scrapbook. Boy, he had it bad.

Mary pulled away from Carl. She went to get the paper

to look up local show times. When she returned, she stood near Wyck. *"Give Love a Chance,"* she read, her voice throaty with innuendo.

"I think Carole Lombard's very trashy," said Faye, trying to sound like the flannel underwear crowd to impress Wyck.

"Carole Lombard's a real she-male, a snappy piece of work, if you ask me," said Carl.

We didn't ask you, Mary thought. She prayed for a reason to stay near Wyck, like glue suddenly dropping from the ceiling or getting her heel caught in his pants cuff.

A small, aproned woman, Elizabeth James, her hair pulled back in the tightest possible bun, brought in some fresh fruit punch. She had a beautiful English accent, cornflower-blue eyes, porcelain skin, and a primness of manner unlike the easy manners of her daughters. Eyeing the ring on Faye's finger, she let her firm hand descend upon the piano keys.

"I told you, my dear," she said in her quiet, strong voice. "Please give the ring back to the gentleman. You are far too young to be trusted with anything of such value."

It's not fair, thought Faye. Her mother pushed boys at Mary because she was five years older and she should marry first. Mary would never find a husband, never, because she was so stuck up.

Tears burned in Faye's eyes, but she gave the ring back to Wyck, who warmed it in his hand, and when Mrs. James left the room, he walked over to Mary and secretly slipped her the sapphire.

"Here," he said. "You take it. It's really meant for you,"

shaking with the honesty of that. "You know, *meant,* in a sss . . . supernatural sense, kkk . . . karmic," tripping over words like furniture in the dark when he got up at night and couldn't find the light.

"Oh, thank you," Mary said. Her voice began where song just ended. Did he like her? Mary wondered, faint with hope. Was it meant to be? Like the times when the lamp went out in the movie projector, or the postman couldn't deliver the serial she was reading because of the snow, it would be a horrible wait to see.

She would have insomnia without eating radishes. Oh, what would happen next?

Chapter 2

■ WYCK PHONED MARY. HE wanted to take her for a ride. Would she like that? Yes, she surely would.

She took him to the Rainbow Box in East Harbor, passing all the crowds from East Harbor going to the Blackhawk Hotel in Felham. You couldn't dance in your own hometown, for freedom was only possible away from your neighbors. You didn't want anyone telling your mom how late you stayed out, joyriding till dawn, smoking, getting blotto, needling the punch, tickling the cola, and who was commode-hugging that night and how loud they played the music and how close you danced. Night after night, half-dressed girls were glued to boys they hardly knew, in syncopated embraces, cheek to cheek, no air separating them except for a swing or a twirl and then back close again, closer than they ever thought possible, and no one would dance with a girl if she wore underwear. Juvenile intrigue. Going their slow, slow rounds of the dance floor with half-closed eyes. Necking and petting in the car afterward. "Pet and Die Young," said the YWCA. She was surprised she was still alive and enjoying her life while her parents slept trustingly through the night.

Her father said, It's your hair, if you want to, bob it. They're your cheeks, if you want to, paint them. And your legs are yours, too, if you want to, shake them. Just don't do any of it in front of me.

Bobbed and painted and shaking her legs, she went to the town next door.

▪

THEY WALKED THROUGH THE crowded door of the Rainbow Box to the huge room where lights skittered across the dancers, and small-talkers screamed to be heard above the sound of glaring trumpets, and waiters shoved their way past groups of table-hopping friends. Wyck was a bit at sea, a paper cup on the ocean of bobbing and gyrating sound. But everyone knew Mary, came up and asked her for a dance, but she led Wyck to a quiet chair on the side.

"Let's just watch," she said, feeling him out to see if he knew how to dance.

He'd have to tell her soon, he thought. He'd only done the waltz, and he could never fake those jiggling limbs out there.

They couldn't talk, the music was too loud.

Is there something wrong with dancing? she was wondering. Did society people let their hair down this far and come unhinged like this?

Wyck sat, the music mixed in his head like sand in summer sandwiches at the beach. What was music anyway? It took something complicated away (your thoughts, your various emotions) and put something back that was simple like—I Miss You, When I Lost You, Y-oo, Just You, There's More to Kiss Than the X-X-X. It made things clearer, sound pushing the world away, noise eclipsing doubt and all confusion.

▪

SHE FIRST MET JAZZ in the Gramophone Department of Gimbel's, Willie Sweatman's clarinet blistering over the loudspeaker, noisier than the crowd of shoppers. It was tough and crass, but humor-raising and hypnotic. She took it home to sing and dance (you couldn't sing to ragtime, but you could sing to jazz, make your voice an instrument expressing all your dreams and moods and sensual desires).

Now jazz was everywhere—symphonic jazz, Broadway jazz, gospel jazz (when Mother wasn't listening), hot jazz, and sweet jazz—they all were habit-forming. Jazz meant being jazzed, and she was a natural dancer, the kind that crowds part for. She knew the words of every song. She could anticipate even the slowest partner, communicating the movements to him, sending it out, her body like a tom-tom, so he could read the message and catch her if she did a swan or swing her if she signaled triple-coil, and she always gave her partner credit even if she danced around him while he did a slow two-step.

Dances and balls were no longer only private (the fox trot, just developed in 1912, had now taken off as a national sport), and the violin had been usurped by the ear-breaking moan of a trombone. Dance music used to be played by amateur groups that never had time to practice, but now the halls had become so popular that real professionals could gather in hotels and make their jazz-a-rhimba numbers perfect for the weekends. They would start out slow and get so fast you'd swear the drummer would not have time to get his stick back from the ceiling for the next beat.

▪

DANCING WAS GOOD BECAUSE you didn't have to talk to your date.

She didn't know what to say to him, after all, he was so different from her, he was still in school (she quit when she was fourteen, and now she had a job) and he lived away from his family (she couldn't imagine leaving home) and he had money (lots of it) and he had brought her an expensive doll (better than flowers since flowers die)—it was a beautiful doll, dressed as a French princess, with pearls on her underpants.

"Do you like to dance?" she asked.

"I don't have anyone to ggg . . . go with all the time," he said.

"I love to dance."

"I have big feet."

"So does Vernon Castle. Do you know that? He wears a size eleven shoe, he has them made just for him, and he can go through four pairs in one night."

"I don't dance anything like Vernon Castle. The similarity ends in shoe size."

▪

"BUT YOU'RE REALLY VERY good," she said.

"Think so?" he asked.

"Yes, I do."

"But not like you." His stutter disappeared when he was happy. "You fly through the air like some kind of kite, and it's as though you make up dancing as you go."

"I do. And I don't. I follow some regular steps. But it's like you charge a battery, you know. I'm part of that band, just playing on myself, sort of submarine, basement-like, not too wholesome and very, very frisky."

"You really look like something out there, Mary, I mean there's not one boy in here who wouldn't want you to be his girl."

"You're full of balloon air, Wyck." The first time she used his name. It was strange to do it. Like a knock on an unknown door.

"I dance like a chunk of lead. A frozen cod. A pooped-out dirigible," he said. "You dance like a star. A helium balloon. A forty-dollar firecracker."

"Is there any such thing?" she asked.

"Yes. I'll take you to see one. And I'll take you to see lots of things, Mary. Have you ever been on an all-night cruise? To Ziegfeld's Midnight Follies? Or the casino in Palm Beach? Or the dog races? Have you eaten snails?"

She didn't want to show her ignorance. The thing was to put on the puppy, be nonchalant. "Yes," she said.

"Oh," he said.

Then she felt bad because, she thought, she had cut off her nose to spite her face. So she tried to make it up to him. She held his hand a lot and snuggled close. She couldn't tell him that she had lied, but she could ask him over every night to teach him dancing (she said), and she tried (though he was not quick to learn), and she gave him self-confidence (God, did he need it), and after a while he began to relax until he had the fox trot and the dog trot, and then he even learned the Bowery hesitation.

It got so they both had fun at the Rainbow Box and at Elysian Field (in another town), and everyone knew them. They had a favorite table, and he bought drinks all the time for everyone and ordered steaks, though she kept "others" from taking advantage of him, "others" being her jealous friends who, envious as they were, started rumors that she was taking ether and triple bromides to dance so well and that she was putting out regularly to have such a rich young man pay so much attention to a no-one, Mary James.

▪

It was getting so he had to make choices. He started to lie at school. He'd never really lied before. His counselor said he noticed that Wyck's car was gone a lot, was he visiting family friends in town?

He wanted to tell his counselor how he'd been feeling. His counselor always asked.

"What are you feeling right now?"

"I . . . I don't know, sir." Inside, Wyck trembled. He felt his counselor read his mind.

"Perhaps you're afraid to tell me how you feel."

His counselor read his mind.

"It's that I fff . . . feel pretty much the same all the time. I sleep. I eat. I go to sss . . . school."

"When you sleep, do you dream?"

Oh yes, he dreamt of Mary, but he couldn't tell the counselor.

The counselor's name was Crosby. There was no way to make this horse drink water. The boy was so defensive. Perhaps a nurse, a woman doctor, could get this boy to talk.

Carl was waiting outside for him. "You'd better not tell him what you're doing, old sport," he said.

"I . . . I know. I know," said Wyck. The secrecy was making him dependent on Mary because their world was nothing he could share.

"I've been thinking," said Carl. "You need to spread your branches. You're acting like a married fella. Let's roll into Newbury and see if we can catch some fish. My cousin knows a few spots to cruise."

"I . . . I've got a date with Mary."

"Criminy. But she's a looker, boy, she is. You could use her to bait us other girls."

"One's fine enough for me," said Wyck.

"Variety, my man. Salt and pepper make a soup taste better, not salt and salt. You should find a girl that's different. Mary's kind of separate. Snobby. You can find a girl that likes to go with crowds."

Mary, after all, had chosen Wyck, not Carl, and even said that he got on her nerves. And Carl missed the days when he and Wyck would roam the roads. Love is for sissies. It makes you lax. It makes you dumb. "She'll ditch you and then you'll come crying back to me," he said and stomped off to work on the dining room wiring.

Wyck went to study mathematics. Counting the hours until he could see Mary. Would she ditch him? Why not? No one in his life had ever stood by him. He thought it would all be so simple once he knew what he wanted. He knew he wanted Mary, but he didn't know that Mary wanted him.

▪

MARY MADE WYCK DINNER at her house one night when her parents drove to Connecticut to visit friends. He remembered the cook at home teaching his sister Peregrine how to prepare a simple family dinner.

"I won't. I can't. I'll never have to do this," Peregrine had said. "There is always a cook."

"What if there's an epidemic?" Aunty argued. "And all the maids are in their beds?"

Aunty hovered over the lesson as Peregrine lit the oven, learned to poach a fish without the head (the cook suggested filleting as a way of life, parts—breasts of chicken, legs of lamb, tails of lobster—were easier for ladies than the whole).

Peregrine was clumsy, and the fish she had served looked like mashed potatoes.

But Mary's meal was elegant. She made him partridge, English style, and as a sweet, a trifle soaked in rum. She served the dinner slowly, sensing when he was ready. When he wanted things. Second courses. Less of something. She filled his wineglass, keeping pace with him.

Nothing he'd ever eaten tasted so fresh and flavorful. Each bite called attention to itself, a valentine in every mouthful. It was cooked for him by loving hands, not by a chef at home or cooks at school who made a hundred meals at once. In the enormity of his heart, which was feeling like the Grand Canyon, he realized this was the first meal in his life that had been cooked by someone who might love him. It was a simple truth but one which rocked his being.

He couldn't tell her. She wouldn't understand. But his gratitude was piling up higher and higher. She had taught him to dance. She could cook him meals. She was very beautiful. She even watched him study, so he was doing well at school.

▪

The beach was so quiet Mary could hear crabs swim in the water and bugs make tunnels in the sand. It had been too good to be true, she thought, just too good, as she sat on the edge of the pier throwing stones at the moon.

She was alone. She had been alone for a week. He hadn't called. They had been out every night for three weeks in a row, hadn't missed a beat, and then one day he didn't call.

When she was little, she used to play hide and seek. She hated to hide, she would giggle, let go of little coughs, let her skirt edge show until she was found. As a matter of course, she began to hide in the same place every time so they would quickly find her out.

She had called him at school. She wanted to say, if you're looking for me, here I am. Please, please find me. And let's go dancing. He wasn't in. He wasn't looking.

Should she repeat the call? Or was it over? Was it something she had done? Had she talked too little or talked too much? He had been late last time. Her nose was running. Had she sulked when they missed the movie? Had she been too critical of Carl? Her heel had broken and she danced without her shoes. Did that make him mad?

She read in the paper that morning of a girl who fell off the Loop-the-Loop at Coney Island. Going up that steep incline in a cart rocking from side to side, slats creaking and shaking on the wooden hill and then with sudden speed, dropping nonstop, whipping and banking, plummeting and screeching—colors paled and pins went through your eyes, your breath in flakes, your stomach turned to splinters, your fingernails were flying off—this girl, spun out, her human life more air than person, helpless and toppling and dying and thinking—Why am I here? But then it was too late.

If you couldn't trust amusement parks, what could you trust? It all confirmed her fears. You could be sure of nothing. Not even the things that people did to have fun.

Was it over? Her and Wyck?

Now you see it. Now you don't.

"Ma-reee . . . Mareeee-Wareeee . . ." It was Faye, calling from across the street. "Guess who's on the phone?"

She dashed across the street and through the yard and into the kitchen.

"Hello," she said.

"Mary," he said. His voice was rough and gravelly. "I've been sick. I had bronchitis. I couldn't call."

"Oh," she said. "I was worried."

"Oh," he said. "I'm all right."

"No," she said. "Not about your health."

"Not about my health?" he asked.

"No," she said.

"What about, then?"

"That you forgot me. Found another girl."

"I'd tell you if I had, Mary. I won't sneak off."

▪

THERE WAS A BIG crowd at the Rainbow Box, and the thing was that a girl came with one boy and then others could cut in. Wyck, still not well, a little weak, watched her a lot.

A cake-walking dervish.

Walking on air.

Carrying the banner.

Cloud climbing.

Grave digging.

Chopping dynamite.

"Ac . . . accelerate your farewell." He couldn't stand it anymore and cut in on some shellacked Boheme who was handing her a line.

He was willing now to be obtrusive with his feelings, stick them out, hold her hand tightly in public, keep his arm around her off the dance floor.

He was getting hooked, no question, getting stuck. He had just gotten his freedom. (The Grove treated him like a college boy. He was realizing what he could get away with, he never tested limits before, always went along with what he knew was safe. Now, with Mary, he tried staying out late, and no one minded, no one even checked to see if he got back.) But he was throwing away his freedom, yes he was, and it felt wonderful, letting his feelings for her boss him around.

Was he in love? he wondered. Love to him had meant going to sleep before it's dark (I love you and I know you need your rest); staying home all the time (I worry about you since I love you); going to the doctor and brushing your teeth and taking bad-tasting medicines. Did you say thank you for the gift? Did you listen (when you didn't want to) to your father? Will you date your sister's friend? Are you proud your brother made it into Harvard (don't you love him)? He must not have understood what love really was. Before he met her his heart was like a boulder placed in front of a cave, blocking out the light, ceasing the flow of ins and outs and life itself. He tried to tell her, but he was too shy.

"Sometimes you talk about things and they go away," he said. "Feelings, I mean, not thoughts."

Why was it so fragile, this thing that was happening between them? Where was the voltage? Where was the shock? This was the Jazz Age, and he had made a wish on every star. He wanted her so.

▪

IT WAS GEORGE BIZET's birthday, and the orchestra was jazzing *Carmen* at the Rainbow Box. The mirrored light was split into a million pieces, the floor mobbed and throbbing like a heart too big for its sac.

They had the dance down perfectly, the Apache tango, effortless, wide, floor-sweeping dips, large fast-steps round the room, ignoring their prostration. They had been dancing three nights in a row and had danced every dance till the orchestra stopped.

Dancing changed your world. It made you feel dizzy and giddy. Brought air to the top of your head and made your mind do somersaults. When she was really breathless and so was he, they looked at each other and that was all they saw, just each other filling their eyes as far as their eyes could see, like water must be to a fish. That was how they knew their love was shared. They were just so satisfied, the eyes, the heart, it was an end to hunger and an end to wanting and it would be that way forever, all moments on a continuum from that moment, and all problems would have this as their solution, and this was the answer to all questions.

She was his girl. He was her guy.

And no one cut in on their dancing anymore.

Chapter 3

■ MARY'S MOTHER DID THE same thing every morning and the same thing every night; in fact, at almost any hour of the day, Mary knew exactly where her mother was, her routine never varying. Mother was in the kitchen now, and Mary and Wyck were helping with the dishes. They always used the special china when Wyck came (he had been there quite a lot, and her mother insisted on serving Wyck with some formality, his, after all, were people who wore tuxedos to small family birthday parties). Mother did the dishes in the old-fashioned way with a pan of soapy water and another pan to stack them in for rinsing. She had a towel for glass and a towel for china and a towel for pots and pans.

Mary was restless. She wanted to go dancing, and the leisurely pace was killing her. Besides, her father had been asking questions about Wyck—did his parents know that he was seeing her? How could he take so much time away from school? How had they met, who did she know who introduced her to a boy like that? She was afraid he'd come in to question Wyck.

But Wyck was zealous, doing dishes was so new for him. He had been taught little of motherly love or human connection.

Mrs. James showed him how to wrap the cream for the window and store the dishes for optimum space. He dropped a cup. He winced and fumbled, old humiliations ringing in his ears. He apologized clumsily.

Mrs. James swept it up with no recriminations, just a sweet smile of acceptance on her face.

"What's it like at your house?" asked Mary.

"I'm not allowed in the kitchen," said Wyck. "The cook gets mad."

Mary asked, "How could she get mad at you? Isn't it your house?"

▪

IN HER MOTHER'S EYES Mary saw a mirror in which time went backward. In that reflection she was Mary who was good and sweet, Mary angel, Mary in the mirror of her mother's eyes, "My little girl is the sweetest girl in the world. Perfectly truthful, mild in manner, always cheerful, tidy, and playful." (This was an age when mothers bent over the cribs of their babies and asked in sotto voices, "Tell me about God, before you forget.")

Her childhood was laced with flowers, fragrant towering lilacs, tall hollyhocks with hummingbirds about them and blackberry blossoms lovely in flower as any clematis.

The Story of Flowers was her favorite book. It broke flowers off into two kinds—one designed by the wind (the grasses), the other (culminating in the orchid) by insects, whose deep probe could create a more complicated, hidden bloom, internal buds, a layered flower with recessed and secret passages, deep cups, flowers that moisten as they reach their centers the way girls and women moisten at their cores.

She was not a grass. Boys were like grasses, seeded by winds, unrare and plentiful and healthy, they dotted the land without the help of hose or hoe. Boys were laid by air.

She tried to imagine Wyck's childhood, but she couldn't. If Wyck couldn't go in the kitchen, where could he go? He spoke of having brothers—did they play cowboys on the good parlor furniture like the boy in the Hubbard house where she worked? Wyck said they did, but he had just watched and hummed the music, mouthed the heigh-ho-horsies.

Wyck was the youngest of four children. His sister, Peregrine, was his immediate senior, and there were two older boys. His eldest brother a Harvard Law School graduate, *cum laude,* William Jr., the youngest in the firm picked to succeed the oldest in the firm, his father. The middle brother, T.C., killed in the European conflict, wearing corporal's stripes. T.C. had inherited (or mimicked) their father's love of war, of railroad timetables and miniature soldiers and battle maps. Their father jumped at any opportunity to ride a horse, attending all parades and carrying colors, and T.C. had jumped, too, north of Arras, where his brain was hit by a German mortar, that brain prepared for Columbia School of International Commerce, now spilled and wasted, soil for French farmers to till their turnips on.

Lost in the shadow of a wall during T.C.'s funeral, Wyck watched his father's lips, waiting to read the words—"Why T.C.? Why not Wyck?"

When he recalled all this for Mary, she argued. Your father loves you. He wouldn't ever say that. You must be wrong. It was impossible that children didn't like their parents or vice-versa.

It was true Wyck never thought of criticizing his father. His father's criticism of him was valid. Proof was on his father's side. Wyck was too shy, too quiet, too fearful to be a lovable son. It was only when he got to the Grove School that his liveliness started to grow inside him. Now it was in full bloom. Now he had Carl to teach him about the things that boys did. And he had Mary to make him want the things that men wanted.

Mary rarely felt the fear-of-father that Wyck had known so long. Her father's presence just implied the boundaries, setting up the outlines for their lives, her mom their balm, their bath, their very content. Dad was there when they were leaving school or starting jobs, ignored their minor illnesses but met the doctor when temperatures got high.

Yet he had sat and stared at her through dinner. What was he thinking, when would he express it, would he interrupt the flow of things, moved forward now?

▪

IN MARY'S SMILING PRINCESS Garden, don'ts were reduced to a minimum. It was all right to go seesawing into the hollyhocks and make mud pies and cookies from freshly turned earth ("Just stay out of the place where Mommie dries her clothes on washday with your dirty hands and feet"). Mary preferred the garden to the dangerous street. Love's little corral. Held prisoner by rose garlands and fairy vines and dandelion chains. There was shade for out-of-door naps in the hottest part of the day, and an arbor that supported a swing, and a slide, and a pergola for tea parties and for climbing when you thought no one was watching.

The smiling garden echoes with the sound of Mary and Faye arguing over who would use the swing. Their sister Sylvia, five years senior to Mary, watched with smug detachment.

You've had it.

It's still my turn.

You take too long.

You don't count fair.

Faye would grab the swing and shake it, but Mary would hold on. Then Faye would start shoving and Mary would flail her legs and try to kick Faye in the face.

Faye was still fighting with Mary.

You stole Wyck away from me.

He didn't have to come to me just because you gave him back the ring.

Mom favors you. She always has.

She does not. She loves us all the same.

I'll show you all. I'm going to marry Footsie Fuller and no one can do anything about it.

Would Dad do something about it? Would he forbid Faye to marry Footsie? Dad didn't like him, but he hadn't stopped their dating, and since he hadn't, why was Mary so afraid that Dad would step in and put an end to her romance with Wyck?

The answer, Mary knew, was Dad's English sense of class. Wyck was different from them in her father's eyes, born into a caste which Mary could or should not join. As a little girl Mary had perceived class in her father's behavior as getting quiet in front of those who did or could employ you, yet this was much more true when Dad had worked at the Athletic Club. Now that he owned his own apartment building, it seemed he judged people differently, had a finer sense of man-to-man behavior, taking each person one case at a time. He was one man with Mr. Hodges, the millionaire banker who gave him the loan, he bowed and seemed diminished in front of him, yet Dad seemed very much equal and at home with Mr. Pritchess, the Odd Fellow in their church whose family, it was said, owned half of West Virginia.

There were reasons not to like Footsie, but they were reasons Dad could chalk up to his being young and American. Footsie carried a hip flask in his front pocket where it showed. He was eight years older than Faye but that only made him twenty-six. He looked a little like Valentino, very dark and swarthy. He had bought Faye some dresses that made her look like a vamp. She slowed her step and thickened her brows and chose a lipstick that was almost brown.

But Footsie was only a Valentino off-hours. Most of the time he worked in a big house near Mrs. Hubbard's on the rich side of town. He did errands and kept the cars for three unmarried brothers. The brothers were all low-lifes, not family people raised in Felham. Footsie sometimes even brought women to the brothers' house.

Faye said the women weren't for Footsie. She had confided in Mary. Mary got jumpy about the trips Faye was making with Footsie to boats in the wharf at night. Footsie would bring in cases, not bottles, whole cases for them to drink, said Faye.

"I don't like it," Mary said.

"Why not? Someone's got to bring it in."

"What if he gets caught and you're with him?"

"Nobody cares. Al Smith rewards people for getting the stuff. Lots of them end up assemblymen or judges."

Faye was dumb. She was taking stupid chances. Hard to imagine, but the oak tree was once a nut.

▪

MARY LIVED A LIFE of trust. Her mother lived a life of faith. She made Mary go to church for twenty-three years. But not every Sunday. When Mary started working for Mrs. Hubbard, she discovered that going one week out of four satisfied her mother.

Mother made faces when things displeased her (although she never complained out loud). Last Sunday morning (the fourth one in a row) Mother made a face and Mary got out of bed.

It was a neighborhood church, across from the Athletic Club, and news had spread that Mary was dating a very rich boy from New York. Mary, obviously the prettiest girl in town, had been the object of a lot of jealous stories. Not only jealous girls talked, but boys whom she'd cold-shouldered.

"Mary is real dumb, that's why she won't go out with anyone. She can't have a conversation. . . ."

"Mary thinks she's too good for us. There's a Blue Book with all the names of society people in it, and Mary sent a letter to them with a picture and some money. That's how she met this millionaire. . . ."

"Mary's parents aren't American. Her mother is from England, but her father is from Bimboland. She's a foreigner like the kind we fought in World War I. . . ."

But the boys still asked her out. Most of the time, she said no. Being bored was better than being disappointed.

Before she met Wyck, she was thinking she might go to New York and get a job. She could ask Mrs. Hubbard if she had any friends in Manhattan. But she knew she would be scared. And why should she go? In search of adventure? Adventure wasn't good for girls.

She had stayed and done things like stand on her toes for twelve-minute intervals three times a day so that her calves would be curved. And it had paid off. The man of her dreams was here in the kitchen right across from her mother, doing the dishes.

Luck-ee Mar-ee. Lucky Maree.

Adventure had walked right into Felham, and while her mother made awful faces at Footsie Fuller, she always had a smile for Wyck.

▪

THEIR MOTHER HAD INSISTED that children were not to be taught. They were their own best teachers. (The principles of Pestalozzi filtering down to Elizabeth James, the value of "letting alone" with supervision.) A mother should observe and not rush in and train. A mother was a soul gardener who used heart insights to guide.

Elizabeth would never accept a gift from the girls if they hadn't made it themselves. The house was cluttered with hand-painted boxes and vases made from food tins and lampshades with yarn pom-poms; a throw rug on the couch had been hand-stenciled to look like zebra fur, and all the family photographs were housed in hand-painted frames. She never put much stock in what the schools were drilling into her girls, and as a result they grew up with few lessons. They were allowed to quit school early and take jobs. She minded that their English was not so proper, but it seemed like the talk of the time. No matter, they could sew and paint and they were good musicians, the kind that played by ear and made up compositions—one a day.

Goldfish were introduced to the United States in 1878 (from China to Korea to Madame Pompadour to Mommie in England and over in the boat), and her mother said she had a baby of that very first goldfish and she let it live in Mary's room. I see you, Fishee, I see you, toys, I see you, Fee Fours (playing cards), I see you, Bishy (her doll), I see you, Mahmee, I see you, Pahpee, I see you, Maree—each night before the lights went out. She kissed her fish bowl and her pictures and her toys and the Cherokee rose painted on her good night set.

She was never afraid of the dark because she fell asleep in her mother's arms and was placed in her crib with no trouble.

Mommie's dearie. Mommie's love.

She left forbidden things alone, but when she was four, Mary touched the little tea set in the dining room (a set of highly colored china, each piece representing a different fruit—the teapot was an apple, the cups a half an orange, a peach, a plum).

Her mother followed her, saying "No," just as she had done before. But Mary persisted in taking off the lids that pleased her.

"Shall Mommie tie up Mary's hands?"

"Yes," said Mary, not knowing what "tie" meant.

Mommie did so very lightly and gently with her handkerchief, more in fun than discipline. It was not Mommie's intention to punish her, for Mommie taught by love.

Yet Mary was surprised. When she saw she couldn't move her hands, she cried and cried, and oh, it hurt her mother to see her cry like that.

"No tie Mary's hands up."

"Well, go find Papa and tell him you are sorry and will not do it again and ask him to take it off."

When her father removed the handkerchief with a kiss, Mary said, "I sorry," not knowing what "sorry" meant.

Care was taken thereafter that even in play nothing would make Mary afraid, but she often walked up to the set of china and looked at it and said, "No Mommie, no tie up Mary's hands," and it hurt her mother every time it happened. She kissed her and held her to her aproned bosom, and said, "My little girl doesn't need to have her hands tied up. My little girl is the sweetest girl in the world."

▪

MARY LOOKED UP. HER father stood inside the doorway. He had let his pipe grow cold and come into the kitchen before the chores were done.

He filled the door, as tall as Wyck, his added bulk and years giving the sense that he was strong and he was right. Not having feared him for a long time magnified the fear that she was feeling now.

Her father turned to Wyck and took the towel out of his hand.

Wyck saw the look of apprehension on Mary's face. Here it was, he thought, all fathers are alike.

"It's awfully late to go out dancing," said Mr. James. "Don't you agree?"

"Www . . . we were just going."

"You both have been very responsible about your hours." He gave Wyck a look of eye-to-eye, no-fooling kinship. "Mom can finish up, go have some fun."

"Thank you, Dad," said Mary, breathing again.

A manly hand upon Wyck's shoulder, Dad said, "We trust you with our little girl."

"I appreciate that, sir," said Wyck to Mr. James.

"Good night, and thank you for coming to dinner," said Mrs. James.

"Thank you for having me," he said, turning to Mary. "It's time for us to go dancing."

She spotted the tea set on the shelf. This very morning she had washed the set and yes, her hands were free.

Chapter 4

SHE HAD BEEN AT the railroad station a hundred times but never at midnight. It was a few miles from her home, and the large wood waiting room with its high-beamed ceiling and well-waxed maple benches was spacious and deserted at that time of night.

Wyck and Mary and Carl and a girl named Kitty Corcoran giggled excitedly as they watched the clock. A toot sounded in the distance, and they ran to the platform and scooped themselves into the oncoming train, flashing tickets at the conductor. The boys had purchased round-trip tickets for the milk train back and forth from Ossining, and now they bribed the porter to let them use the deluxe Pullman compartment, riding empty in the night.

"Wait until all those trollops and greaseballs get a load of this," said Kitty.

Mary was self-conscious. Carl always had a new girl with him, and this one, Kitty, wore a beaver coat and chain-smoked Sobranies (she called them brain tablets), her language filled with slang expressions. "Eye it. Try it. Buy it," and "Cuddle that in your canopy."

Mary had been trying to cut out her slang, correct her English. Before she met Wyck it had seemed smart to talk "street language." Slang was like jazz itself—speech percussive like good drums. "Is you?" "Ain't you?" had a swing, and double negatives like "I don't need no" gave emphasis. Her mother's speech was so constrained, like keeping talk within a box, checkers in their squares. But Wyck talked violins and chamber music, and class was when you had it even though the king of England wasn't listening.

"Want some?" Carl asked Kitty as he unstrapped a bottle of hooch hidden in his wide trousers.

"I'll say she does," said Kitty.

"Football gin," said Carl. "One drink and you kick off."

Carl reached for the Pullman bed, and Wyck went to help him, slamming himself against the compartment wall when the bed came down abruptly.

Carl started sifting hungrily through Kitty's clothes, trying to find her body. "Oh"—she giggled—"for crying out lewd."

"*Très* uncouth," said Mary.

"It's *très* fun," said Carl, pinning Kitty to the narrow bed.

"Where are the cards?" asked Mary.

"Why do you want to play ccc . . . cards?" asked Wyck, his nervousness causing the stutter that Mary had not heard for a while.

He had always been the kind who, while shy, would try anything he could at first, try to get it over with, get the "No" up front, ending it right there. But he wanted to keep things going with Mary, had known that when he met her, so he pretty much kept his hands off her, making only gentle suggestions like, "If you'll be real nice to me, I'll let you drive." And when she showed no signs of wanting more than good-night kisses, he let her drive anyway. Up to now, they had mostly touched while dancing, but their good-night kisses had gotten longer and his hands had started traveling down her body as he said goodbye.

"I've only known you a month," said Mary.

"But you lll . . . like me?" he said.

"Yes, I like you a lot," she said.

"Mary, you're so natural and things just seem to ccc . . . come out of you so easy. When you dance and when you talk. I admire you, Mary," said Wyck. "I th . . . think I'm falling for you."

"That's some line," said Mary. "But I'm not the kind of girl who lets a boy touch her all over when she hardly knows him."

"Then let's jjj . . . just talk," he said.

"Fine," said Mary and they sat together in awkward stillness.

"Mary," he said, he couldn't stand the silence.

"Yes," she said.

"I've taken vvv . . . very few girls out. I mean, most of the time it's been at dances or parties, like that."

"Oh," she said.

"The schools I went to hhh . . . had all boys."

"Hmmmmm," she said. She didn't want to appear more worldly than he, but she was.

"Mary," he said, just shoving the question out at her. "What's it like?"

"What?" asked Mary.

"It. You know," said Wyck.

"How do you know I know?" asked Mary.

"I know," he said. "I can tell."

"It doesn't make you think I'm bad or something?" asked Mary.

"No, it . . . it makes me think you're a real woman," said Wyck.

"When I did it," said Mary, "I was engaged."

"What was his name?" asked Wyck.

"Eddy Rose," said Mary.

▪

FOUR YEARS EARLIER, ON a similar night, Eddy Rose had asked her to a Camouflage Party, the very latest in entertaining, reflecting the military spirit of the period. The patriotic home front theme. Made in U.S.A.

> You are commanded to appear at 8 o'clock on the evening of Saturday, November 16, 1916, at the regimental headquarters, 234 State Street, and be prepared to go at once to the Front. If you are unable to appear due to physical disability or other causes, please notify the Staff or Recording Officer.

The word "camouflage" meaning to deceive, to throw dust in the eyes, everyone came as a tree or a village or a river. Mary painted a sheet blue and glued little boats on it, and Eddy came as an airplane, proudly letting his new army uniform show beneath. The women were given men's jobs and vice-versa under penalty of going to the Guard House. Red-Cross-costumed and Hoover-aproned girls presided over a knitting table, where Eddy had to knit a few stitches on a muffler and then apply first-aid bandages to a window-display model. Mary made bayonet charges at a hay-stuffed dummy labeled "This is the Kaiser," and also initiated herself into the intricacies of semaphore code.

At a self-service dinner in "The Mess Hall," they ate off tin plates. The food suggested an army diet: pork and beans and war bread and stewed dried fruits. Eddy sang the army song "Soupy, Soupy, without a single bean."

There were signs saying, "The only good Hun is a dead Hun," and they debated questions like "Did Wilson stay out of the war too long?" or "Is it Christian to hate the Hun?" Then someone did a monologue burlesquing Kaiser Wilhelm. They danced the Rosalie—a front line name for a bayonet (very simple and very direct)—and then they went back to the living room, where a sign said, "Closed for the Kaiser's Funeral."

There were trenches in the yard—made of porch furniture and blankets—and everyone sat in them and thought about lightless edicts and months of searching the daily casualty lists for the names of boys who were at that party.

She and Eddy climbed into one of those trenches. It was very still, and they pretended they were in Europe surrounded by the Huns. Then it got very quiet, and Eddy whispered to her about the Russian Death Squads over there and why the boys were marching, and his breath was very warm and tropical . . . over there . . . he was actually trembling and very afraid of dying and getting his legs shot off, and he asked her, after all, he would marry her when he got back from over there, but would she go with him just this one time to the car, it would be very patriotic of her, after all, it was her duty.

▪

WYCK HID HIS UPSET. He burned with feeling jealous. If he were going to war, would she do it with him? (Had his brother T.C. done it?) Boys were lucky then, they had a real excuse.

"What was it like?" he asked, knowing he didn't really want to hear.

"Like being caught in a waterfall, crashing down a hill, being washed out to sea, but everything is warm and loving and even though it seems you don't belong to you, you do." She stopped. "Talking about it makes me blush, but that's what it's like. A big blush all over your body but nothing delicate or ladylike because you make a lot of noise and all."

Chapter 5

■ IT WAS SOME DAYS before Christmas and a long, black limousine pulled up in front of the James house, dwarfing the street. Wyck's luggage was piled in the back. He was going home for Christmas.

A tight-lipped driver in a black uniform with a cap watched coldly as Wyck walked up the stairs to the house. Mary, in ecru crepe and pearls, slid out the door. Her cape fit like a calla lily around her neck. She was gorgeous. She was stunning.

They were off to Broadway to see a play, the hit of the season, *Abie's Irish Rose.* Can Catholic marry Jew? Can rich and poor live happily together? The most popular play of the year said yes.

When they were back in the limousine after the show, Wyck drew the isinglass curtains. He held Mary in his arms. She was dazzled. In love.

"I want to stay overnight in New York," she said, an inspiration, not knowing she was going to say it.

"Where?" said Wyck.

"In a hotel. That'll make the evening perfect," Mary

said. "I'm going to stay at the Marie Antoinette."

"The one on Sixth?" said Wyck.

"I once peeked inside. It's like a theater in itself," she said. (Decor by Schiaparelli, M-G-M, and Mesmer.)

"Let me stay with you," said Wyck.

"I couldn't do that," said Mary, but his kisses ran like ruffles down her throat, and (hoping that the driver was not looking in the rear-view mirror) he let his hand travel up between her legs like a velvet butterfly, it fluttered there and they were kissing very strongly now. She knew what a hot-air balloon must feel like as it is being filled, because that is what she felt like, down between her legs, and she half expected her skirt to rise up from the heat. He kept kissing her, his face angelic and very sweet, there was a glow, an aura about him, and he had that great athletic neck, those veins and cartilage that ran like cables to his chest. He was a true *rara avis,* like no one she had ever met, and she loved him and she loved his kisses and she knew she was going to love whatever else. He reminded her of the room price at the Marie Antoinette, and she used it as an excuse to give in.

▪

THE OPERATOR OF THE hotel elevator wore a wig and a satin waistcoat. He stared ahead while Mary and Wyck tried to look like an old married couple. When the door slid open, they tiptoed down the elegant hallway.

Mary stopped. "Maybe we should have a cup of tea," she said.

"Do you really want one?" Wyck asked.

"No," she said, and started walking again. "I'm just scared."

"Don't be scared," he said, scared himself.

"Maybe we should go back," she said.

"I paid already," he said, wanting to go back himself.

The door stood in front of them, and he fumbled with the key, finally unlocking it and pushing it open into a mirrored suite—crystal chandeliers, hand-painted furniture, a heavenly dome in blue and pink silks with toothy cupids of Dresden flesh holding back cascades of teal-blue taffeta.

Mary was stunned into silence.

She took off her shoes and sank into the deep, soft rug. The bed had been turned down by the staff.

She was transformed.

They reached for each other, and they kissed, and he whispered something in her ear. His voice was like the ocean sound captured in a seashell, her ear, a conch resounding from his breath. A roar began between the two of them, and it got louder and deeper as their breathing and their bodies rose and fell. There were a million sea creatures moving and shouting to make themselves heard through the sound of waves getting higher and water getting deeper and she was diving and coming up for breath and water poured all over her and she was drowning and coming up and going down.

It lasted for hours.

It was nothing like it was with Eddy.

This was true love and she told him, "I love you."

Should the girl say it first? She didn't know, maybe she should have waited. She saw his eyes tear over.

"I shouldn't have said that," she said.

"I'm just not used to having this much feeling. Love, or what I thought it was at home, has been heavy-hearted, massive, formal. You make me feel simple, just so happy."

"I'm happy too."

"A girl has never said I love you to me before."

"I do. I love you. Family feelings are different from what we feel for each other. This is romantic love. I couldn't use the word anymore without thinking of you. It's both of us. Two things put together. It's something you have to dip or soak before it's good, like crullers, or French bread in roast beef juice. It's cake and tea. Girls and perfume. Ocean and air."

"I love you, Mary," he said. He meant it, too. He was so happy. And so was she.

Sex was invented that night. It was as if no one in the world had done it so lovingly as they. It seemed as if no one in the world had ever loved as much as they. It was the most romantic night in the world.

▪

THE TRADITIONAL CHRISTMAS DAY dinner at the Hanover mansion. The rooms were filled with important furniture, distinguished politicians, social leaders, and churchmen, the heads of all the brokerage houses, real estate companies, and mortgage firms, because William Hanover was close to all those things: Wall Street, real estate, and banking. William Hanover owned 95 million dollars' worth of New York property.

The Right Reverend Daniel Hanover of Philadelphia said a long grace as the guests sat at the tables laden with freshly shot game birds from Hanover homes, fruit puddings baked from Hanover recipes three hundred years old, ornately jeweled and silver platters released from Hanover vaults.

Old money. Old power. This was a visible family. Charter members of the Social Register, patrons of the arts, limousine-driven to multiple houses in multiple countries. The Hanover clan was led by Wyck's father. The Major. Bombastic, a horn with boundless, compulsive energy. He used the word "fool" all the time.

Wyck's sister and brother, Peregrine and William Jr., were at home in society, like championship ice skaters gliding in and out of conversations, sipping mulled cider, talking about light metal futures and the Russian Boys' Choir.

"Wyck, you remember Cousin Beatrix," said Peregrine, her smile beaming don't-ruin-this-you-clod. Peregrine talked to him as though he were a child who refuses to learn his lessons. If Peregrine could pick a wife for him, she'd pick someone like this girl. A distant cousin, lacking grace or magic, but dependable and churchgoing. Mary with his family would be an unwanted spark in dry savannah igniting strong, destructive fires.

"I've seen you in the country," Beatrix said to him, "but you haven't attended the fall dances, have you? I've noted your name printed in the programs." She stopped suddenly, afraid of giving away one of her debutante secrets—you were supposed to make a list of all the boys who hadn't pledged to girls. Then you coupled your name with someone's and prayed over it. Mrs. Beatrix Hanover—she had played it over in her mind.

"I . . . I board in Connecticut," said Wyck.

She knew. She even knew that he was considered dull-witted by his family, but then she herself had been marked for spinsterhood. God had made her head too large, her eyes in need of glasses, and her breath, no matter what she used, reeked of postdigested meals.

"I am in the Ladies Academy at Marley, although my mother worries about my being away from home." The words came in rasps because she was trying not to breathe on him as she spoke.

"Th . . . there's a lot to worry about, I suppose," said Wyck. He was worrying himself. Would Mary change her mind and not meet him at the suite?

"I'm having friends up to New Year's dinner," Beatrix said. "Would you like to come?"

"Thank you, but I'm going back to school," said Wyck. He saw the ease with which he lied. Maybe it would be easier than he thought to have a life separate from his family. Falling in love had come so naturally. Mary had appeared from nowhere. If she had come to him like this, maybe God was apologizing, making up for burdening him with the differences that made his family not accept him.

"I . . . I have to go now," he said to Beatrix.

"Yes, you *all* do," she said and snuck another mint into her mouth.

Wyck hurried toward the door, but was stopped by a man wearing the blood-red ribbon of the Légion d'Honneur on the lapel of his tuxedo. "How is, ahem, college?" asked the man, his patronization of Wyck not well hidden.

"It's fff . . . it's fff . . ."

"Fine, yes, fine," the man finished the sentence for him and then asked, "I say, do you know what the market closed at yesterday?"

"No." Wyck shook his head.

"Stocks are so volatile at Christmas."

"I . . . I'm afraid I don't read the *Journal.*"

"You're certainly not your father's son, my boy," he said, and turned toward the bar.

Out of place in his own home, Wyck left quickly and went to the hotel, where Mary would be waiting for him. Mary was his society. With her he was clever, handsome, and fun.

▪

THOMAS CROSBY, THE COUNSELOR from the Grove School, had been sent by the headmaster to inquire after the whereabouts of Edward Wyck Hanover. Although his condition had improved greatly since the fall (his blood pressure had risen from a scant 100 to a normal rate, and his speech had improved), he had appeared tired of late and, since returning from Christmas holiday, had spent a great many weekends away from the school. The Hanover family seemed uninterested. Yes, Wyck was given a car. Yes, his checks arrived by mail and they were generous, but his father and aunty were only seen once, the day they delivered the boy to school, and he had had only one visitor, his sister and her fiancé right before their marriage. All this the headmaster had gone over with Mr. Crosby before instructing him to set a meeting with the Jameses, at which it could be explained just how important the Hanover family actually was.

Mrs. James agreed to meet with Mr. Crosby, not telling her husband of the call. She did not wish to alarm him, he was, after all, a moralist who felt the twentieth century was a fad. Her urge for universal peace made her keep her own counsel.

When Mr. Crosby asked her about Wyck, she admitted

that the young man was a frequent visitor to their home, but said that she did not ask many questions after his whereabouts. (In fact, she did not ask many questions about her daughter either. There had always been a looseness to her thinking with the girls. Sleeping out did not arouse her suspicions. They baby-sat. They lived in homes and cared for very old and very young. She did not keep close track of them, feeling that they would never frustrate the grace of God. Her girls knew better than she how to act in this strange country, in these strange times.)

Crosby tried to give her thinking a more precise direction. "Wyck's absence from school may be more serious than you think. The Grove is for boys with various problems. When Wyck came to us, he had serious nervous disorders, he stuttered a great deal, he was painfully self-aware."

"We haven't noticed any of these things," said Mrs. James.

"He's shown great improvement and lost much of his reserve," said Mr. Crosby.

"Then it seems he's chosen a life that really suits him," said Mrs. James, with no edge and with characteristic patience.

Crosby tried a conspiratorial tone. "You and I might see that, Mrs. James," he said, "but we both know the family would be most upset if they knew that Wyck was spending so much time with a girl."

"We don't know that at all. They seem not to show much interest in the boy. I understand the purpose of your visit and I believe you are good-hearted. But so are we and so is my daughter, Mr. Crosby. She has his best interest at heart, and it is not my nature to spoil that."

Mrs. James dismissed him politely and put the meeting as far out of her mind as she could. She felt the Hanover family could look after themselves. In fact, she wondered why this Crosby was investigating Wyck. It was not his station, the family had not asked him to. She had been brought up to accept the ways of wealthy people, and even though she was no longer a servant, as she had been in England, it was too ingrained an attitude for her to change. Keep your place, it's a source of comfort.

She never expected Wyck to marry her daughter. She felt the rich should stay with the rich, and she identified with how his family would feel. But there was such a poignancy about this boy, he seemed so much at home within their home, that she forgot her fears and let Mary spend a lot of time with him. After all, she didn't like the local boys, and here was something finer, someone tender who had seen more than Felham High School, Felham Park. He was so obvious about wanting to be there, so clear in his desire to be with them instead of his own family, that she was compelled to help him, let him in the door, this motherless child so much in need of a mother.

Chapter 6

IN THE BATHROOM OF their suite at the Marie Antoinette, through silk hose dangling over the curtain rod, Wyck was bathing Mary. The bubbles were disappearing, and her nakedness showed beneath. He blew the rest of the bubbles away. She poured in more of the L'Eau d'Etoile (she had already added colored sugar to the water) and turned the faucet on hard. Bubbles rose into his mouth. His crepe de chine bathrobe was drenched. He climbed into the tub, robe and all.

This was not their second trip to the Marie Antoinette. It was their fifth. And, like she taught him dancing, she had taught him sex.

▪

AFTER THE FIRST SUCCESS, there had been failure. They were in bed and everything seemed to be fine, but it didn't get like it usually did. It just lay there, reminding him of a frog's throat going kind of glump, soft, the skin moving but not making it turn into anything the way it should. He thought, what is wrong? The more he thought, the softer it got. Then he said, pardon me, I need to get a glass of water, but she knew something was up, or wasn't, and it scared her, too, but thank God, she didn't feel insulted. (She said, Sometimes our need to be together, close and intimate, gets too overwhelming, like a cozy fire suddenly turning to a burn that could take down a house. And he couldn't always be a superman or athlete, he had a right to be nervous. But this was the first time it showed in bed.)

He got in next to her, afraid to try it again. Despite what she said, he had heard about things like this, impotence, and he thought it was a curse, and all kinds of things kept running through his mind, but she laughed and said something about Lazarus rising again.

In fact, she was so understanding, she took him to all-night dances and midnight movies so there would be no opportunity for sex. She stressed the spiritual side of their affair, reading Edgar Guest and Thomas Hardy until he couldn't keep his mind on the words, and all he could think of was her sitting there across the room (he liked her body dressed, it overwhelmed him in the nude, he liked to make love best underneath the sheets). He wanted so to touch her, he begged, but she wouldn't let him. (A trick, she'd picked this up from a magazine—"How to Awaken Natural Desire.") Finally, one night, when he was begging, threatening, she gave in, and his desire rose as high as the man in the moon, a million birds, a May cloud, a lightning rod, an air corps rocket.

▪

MARY DECIDED SHE SHOULD study about sex, it was not to be taken for granted, here was a subject she should take a look at.

Her sister, Sylvia, five years older, was a prude. She married young, a virgin, after all, that was years before the war, before the vote, before dancing.

Mary said, "I am not a virgin. I had sex with Eddy Rose."

Sylvia closed her eyes and made a horrible face as though she were going to hit her, and then she prayed a little under her breath and said to Mary, well, she only did it once, that meant she was almost-a-virgin, and if she kept her mouth shut (too late for that), Wyck need not know until their wedding night.

Not a virgin once. Not a virgin twice. Not a virgin three or four times. Mary tried to listen as Sylvia gave her all these reasons why she should remain chaste:

1. Girls who are not virgins regretted having done it.
2. Contrary to what men sometimes said in the heat of passion, all of them wanted to marry virgins.
3. Your husband would not respect you.
4. It always got out and your reputation was wrecked.
5. Once you did it with one man, you did it with another, and then you felt promiscuous and unfit for marriage, and you would lead the rest of your life in loneliness.
6. You would get pregnant (contraception never worked when you needed it to).
7. If she did it, she would be under horrible strain because of a greater need for self-control once her erogenous zones had been aroused, and she couldn't see him often enough to relieve herself with sufficient frequency or to complete the act without worry.

8. She would have the burden of psychic stress, circulatory congestion, nervous tension, disordered functioning of the ductless glands, plus the emotional problem of knowing that what she was doing was totally against the wishes of her family, her neighbors, and even Jesus himself.

Mary didn't argue with her sister, in fact, she told her that they were all terrific reasons. But they didn't matter, wouldn't matter the next time she and Wyck were together. Her sister didn't know how tempting it was and how lovely it was, and she had heard that there were ways to make it better. She wanted to do that for him, make it better each time, to show him how she loved him, it was a chance to translate feelings, like speaking in a different language, or transposing tunes from voice to keys. So, for her, Mary James, she had determined that she would put her useless thighs on springs and open those legs which she had locked for twenty years (almost). She was a member of the New Generation, and, she told her sister, since she was going to do it anyway, why not learn to do it well?

▪

SYLVIA FINALLY WENT WITH her to the Purity Drug Store and, flashing her wedding ring, purchased a book in a plain brown wrapper which the salesman drew from beneath the counter.

Rational Sex Lives by Helena Hall, M.B., B.S., with an introduction by the Reverend William J. Robinson, D.D. She skipped to the good part, "The Perfect Sex Act."

"All lovers need to be courted afresh every time they

seek each other out. Every complete act of love follows a definite pattern. First, it is necessary to have an atmosphere of peace and leisure."

She would play a little game with him (her mother had taught it to her), "Giving Your Troubles to Jesus." She would take a handkerchief and ask him what his troubles were, and then, one by one, she would lay them on the square and tie it up and put it in the other room, leaving all his cares outside.

Next, as Helena Hall instructed, she would leave the room in semilight. "It is a pity that couples so often choose to make love in the dark. In a subdued light the lovers can watch each other's faces, telling by their expressions whether they are fulfilling each other's wishes or not.

"Words play the first part in kindling ardors, to awaken a desire is a poem in itself. . . . As Pygmalion knew, the real woman of flesh and blood can be released by making love," said the book. And it was true. Mary couldn't believe what kisses, smiles, a glance could do. She often dreamt of "The Nutcracker"—the tale of toys come out to play at night. That's what lovemaking was like to her. Putting life into something not already living. Making dreams come true.

"There is a precise sequence of arousal, which, if followed, assures that the response will be more ardent.

"First is the region of the mouth and face, as well as the base of the neck and the lobes of the ears. The earliest sign of response is flushing of the cheeks; if this occurs, success generally follows. The second area is the chest or breast, especially the nipples, which become erect under the tender caresses of a lover's lips or fingers."

Mary wished she could become transported without having to get messed up. She remembered her Tessie-doll, her expression never changed when you removed her clothes. She had that same unruffled look, her dresses on or off. Her skin did not mottle and her mouth did not swell. Oh, she wanted to be perfectly beautiful for him.

"The whole body should now be awake and ready for direct stimulation of the sex organs themselves. It is necessary for the love-flight to think of music, for it is here that rhythm plays an important part."

Mary practiced rhythms, movements, humming jazz tunes and even swinging to "The Surprise Symphony." She soon found in their love play that quick movements were too exciting for Wyck, and so she stuck with the slow tunes—"Love Will Find a Way," "All by Myself." It was like dancing. You couldn't spend it all too fast. She took to sex as a long-distance dancer takes to the road.

"The question of positions is an important one," the book continued. "It is essential that organ contact be maintained, and it is best if both partners can move their hips freely; but within these limits a great deal of variety is possible":

a. By far the position most often adopted by Europeans is face to face with the man on top and the woman on her back.
b. Vice-versa.
c. In classical Rome, the attitude of the wife astride was greatly favored.
d. In the sedentary attitude, the man sits while the woman faces him, sitting on his lap, her legs around his waist.

e. In the side-to-side attitude, success depends on the relative proportions of the pair and, therefore, in some cases it is impossible.
f. In the position from behind, the man is behind the woman, who can be either standing up or lying down.

Mrs. Hall encouraged her readers to experiment. "Sex ought to be an art. Monotony is the deadliest enemy of love."

▪

"WE'RE SO DIFFERENT," SHE said to him one night.

"Yes, we are," said Wyck.

"You'd think we couldn't talk to each other, wouldn't you, hon?" she asked.

"But we can," he said, giving her a hug. "It's like a rose and a pea, fitting in a pod."

They talked about things that were in the papers. Mary kept him up on stories he missed because he was studying for school. A gambler was murdered, but so many people had wanted to kill him that the police quit trying to find out who did it. And Charlie Chaplin had married a girl so young she had to be tutored after the wedding or he'd be in contempt of court.

"Maybe when you are your own boss, you could get me a tutor," she said. She dreamt of his coming of age and breaking with his family. She never broached the subject directly, but used phrases like "when you are your own boss."

He wondered what Mary wanted. They couldn't stay this way forever, and he knew it. One day she might want to be married more than she wanted to be in love. Would she leave him if he never talked of marriage?

Faye and Footsie had set a date for their wedding. Faye had refused to see him until he proposed to get married. For five weeks she hadn't answered his calls. Finally, he sent a telegram proposing. But Mary wasn't like Faye. She couldn't face losing Wyck. What if he never came back to her?

She wanted to ask him outright, Please marry me. I know your father has all the money and you won't get it for years. But I don't care. We could both work. All I've ever wanted is you. When we met, I knew that. And Sylvia had been right—making love to him, she wanted more love. Like breastfeeding, the more a mother nursed, the more milk came. So she planned their "love-flights" and learned the art of concealing art.

And when she asked herself—am I doing this from joy or am I doing this from fear? Is sex a snare, addicting him to love?—she turned to Mrs. Hall's little handbook to try to ease her guilty conscience.

"It is often the wife's turn to take the initiative. However active a man's nature may be, the time inevitably comes when he is tired and lacks, for the moment, the energy to commence lovemaking. This is the wife's opportunity to show her many-sided nature, wooing him and charming him out of his fatigue."

If she left out the word "wife," it all seemed very Scott-Fitzgeraldy. The book reeked of modern doctrine. "For one reason or another, mental hedges have been allowed to grow up around the subject of sex in America. The average attitude toward sex is unhealthy, ignorant, and thoroughly unsatisfactory.

"There are, however, signs of improvement. More and more people are coming to understand why it is important to have a happy sex life. Authorities on the mind are telling us that lack of sexual satisfaction is a potent source of illness. Freud has taught us that repression of the sexual instinct is dangerous."

It all fit in with the flapper credo, expressed by magazines and movies and everything else she believed in. Sex is good for your health. It's terrible for your mind not to kiss a lot. And be of love so careful. It's better than anything. Study for it. Groom for it. Rehearse it and memorize it long into the night. Be of love so careful.

▪

WYCK HAD BEEN GIVEN *What a Young Boy Ought to Know* by Sylvanus Stall, D.D. (handed to him at age eleven by his father with the untranslated Latin murmur *Post coitum omne triste*), published in Philadelphia by the Vir Publishing Company in 1905. "The information contained in this little book is all that any boy needs to know until he arrives at the age of eighteen," it said, a part of the Self and Sex Series, dedicated to "the thousands of boys whose honest inquiries concerning the origin of life deserve such a truthful, intelligent, and satisfactory answer as will save them from ignorance, enable them to avoid vice, and deliver them from solitary and social sins."

There were no good parts.

He read it several times, from beginning to end, but could find nothing about how sex actually was done. There was a lot about being born.

"In order that you may fully understand the mystery of the beginning of life, I am going to read to you from a booklet written by Dr. Alice Wood-Allen, a noble, pure-minded Christian mother who narrates the following conversation between a thoughtful little boy and a mother who wisely prefers to teach her child the truth rather than to leave him to the polluting influences of the school or the street.

" 'Mamma, how big was I when I was made?' asked the boy.

" 'When you were made, my dear, you were but a tiny speck, not so big as the point of a needle.'

" 'Why, Mamma, if I were as small as that I should think I would have been lost.'

" 'So you would have, dear child, if the kind Heavenly Father had not taken special care of you. He knew how precious little babies are, and so He made a little room in mother's body, where they can be kept from all harm until they are big enough to live their own separate lives.'

" 'How long was I in that room, Mamma?'

" 'Three-quarters of a year, and you grew and grew every day. Because I wanted you to be happy, I tried to be happy all the time, and I was careful to eat good food so that you might be strong. I tried to be gentle, kind, patient, persevering, in fact everything I wanted you to be.'

" 'Yes, Mamma, and how did I get out?'

" 'When the time came for you to go out into the world, the door of your little room opened, with much pain and suffering to me, and you were born.' "

Had he made his mother suffer? Had he made her sick? Was that why she died?

His mother's room when she was ill was like a womb, the shades were closed and voices sifted through your ears as though they were stuffed with wadding. But what had mother's door looked like? She was so frail, how could he have grown inside her (how does the model ship get into the bottle)? Did she get the speck by sipping him the way she sipped lemonade through an invalid straw? Was the door in her stomach (or near her knees as his sister said)? Where was the entrance, was it like the cave of Ali Baba and you had to know a secret word? Was it like their family vault hidden behind an oil painting? Did it appear like the rabbit's hole in the earth appeared for Alice?

His mother, so romantic, seldom out of bed, her social appearances so rare that people would gather around her, staring as if she might disappear. Women imitated her whiteness (she looked as though a candle burnt within her), calling the color Inner Parafin, Couleur de Camille, or Michelangelo White (marble statues, painted before the time of Michelangelo, had by then become rain-washed, and art lovers realized they were more beautiful without the paint). Voices hushed when she was near, and women curtsied slightly (though they hated themselves afterward for doing so), and children stopped to ask, "Who is that lady? She is so celestial, so ethereal, as though she is visiting us from Heaven."

When people died, did they become little specks again, go back into an inner cradle, a soft chamber, warm within a womb? God opens mother's door when we are born to let us out, and when it's time for us to go back to Him, He opens His own door and all His grown-up specks climb right up. Was his mother cozy now, between the legs of God?

▪

HE KNEW SEX MUST have something to do with "the mystery of the beginning of life," and so, like a detective, he put together clues. For instance, on page 76 the Reverend talked about Mama and Papa "being twain in one flesh." But all it said was: "I have already told you that since the creation all forms of life begin with an egg. The egg or ovum, when formed in the body of a woman, is very small. The same is true of the spermatozoa or life germs, contained in the fluid called semen that forms in the body of a man, and by which, in the state of pure and holy marriage, God has ordained that the ovum, while yet in the body of the wife, shall be fertilized by the requisite and proper bodily contact of the husband."

It never said what the requisite and proper bodily contact was.

▪

EVERY SUMMER WYCK'S FAMILY took the railroad to Manitou Springs in Colorado, which boasted sixteen baths containing herbs and minerals, many of which tasted like dried cod and smelled like rotten eggs.

Wyck was in the children's spa with a little boy and a little girl around his age, age six. They were alone in the shallow pool, the three of them, when the girl said to him, "Show me yours. I'll show you mine."

"I don't have any," said Wyck.

The boy said, "Yes, you do have one. You have one of these." He pulled down his water-soaked bathing trousers to show Wyck what he meant. It floated in the water like a blown-up worm.

The girl put her hands over her eyes, but peeked out through her fingers.

"I've stuck it in her," the boy said. "In the water, right here."

"You stuck it in her?" asked Wyck.

"That's what grownups do. They do it all the time," he said.

"I'd never do a thing like that," said Wyck.

"Your father and your mother do," the boy insisted.

"They do not," said Wyck.

Hanovers were not supposed to talk about bodies. God (Who always listened) might be offended. Hanovers had been instructed to cover themselves totally so that God (Who always watched) would not be displeased.

When they returned from Colorado, he asked his mother (trying to be casual because he knew he shouldn't speak of bodies, at a time when she didn't have a headache because he thought this might cause her one), "A bbb . . . boy told me . . . told me . . . Did . . . Ddd . . . Dad . . ."

"Daddy what?" his mother asked.

"Did Ddd . . . Ddda . . . Ddd . . ." he couldn't get it out.

"Speak up, dear. Don't be shy."

"Did . . . did Ddd . . . Daddy stick his thing in you?" he blurted out.

His mother paled (the first sign of a headache). "Who told you that? We'll call and have him punished."

"I don't know his nnn . . . name," said Wyck.

"As for what you said, you're far too young to know,"

she said, but then her stern tone softened and she smiled. "I'll tell you later."

There was no later.

▪

THE REST OF THE book had chapters titled "Man Is an Animal," "Man is the only animal with a perfect hand," "With the hand he constructs, builds, and blesses his fellows; with the hand he smites, slays, and injures," "With the hand he pollutes and degrades himself."

It had quotes from First Corinthians about spilling yourself, and it said, "Instead of using their hands as intelligent and moral beings, some boys use their hands so as to pollute their bodies by handling and toying with their sexual member in such a way as to produce a sensation, or feeling, which may give a momentary pleasure, but which results in the most serious injuries to the moral, intellectual, and physical powers, and such a use is called self-pollution or masturbation."

His uncle, the bishop, scratched his balls. His grandfather used to swear by holding his hand on his testicles instead of his heart ("testicles" coming from the Latin variant of "tile" or "earthen vessel used for testing"). In school, the boys all shot their pee and measured how far it went. They measured their "things" too, in the showers, took wooden rulers and competed for "Best Erection" (keeping in mind the school motto, "Your will can make you a genius").

"I can say, however, that many pure-minded boys learn the habit of masturbation in innocent ways. Many boys discover the sensation by sliding down banisters, climbing and descending trees, or, because of an uncleanness of the sexual member, they have experienced itching and when relief has been sought by rubbing, have been introduced to the habit of self-pollution.

"If the habit is long continued, the entire nervous system will eventually become shattered and ruined beyond all hope. If the body is naturally strong, the mind may give way first, and imbecility and insanity may, and often do, come as the inevitable result. Where the body is not naturally strong, a general wasting may be followed by consumption or life may be terminated by any one of many diseases.

"In order to prevent masturbation, and if possible, permanently to cure the victim of this vice, boys often have to be put in a strait-jacket, sometimes have their hands fastened behind their backs, sometimes their hands are tied to the posts of the bed, or are fixed by ropes or chains to rings in the wall."

Well, you can bet he never touched his pecker, no, not him. Not at all.

▪

UNTIL MARY HELPED HIM to forget Dr. Stall, then he got over his fear of touching it and touching her, and he loved his seed and let it spill all over everything in spite of First Corinthians. It was New York and 1921 and he was eighteen, and he didn't believe in Dr. Stall anymore.

He believed in Mary James.

▪

SHE HAD NATURE'S GIFT of easy orgasm. He gave nothing away easily, held it tight within himself like a reel, curled up, and he would let it out slowly, he would let it out so slowly, but in their loving he would finally let it go, and for the first time in his life he could trust completely, let down all defenses, unguarded and unworried, like a newborn baby coming down the chute, gasping and gagging, taking air in gulps, he would come shouting and screaming to Paradise.

They would lie as though levitated (she had seen that once), their bodies drifting like streamers gently blown out from a fan. He would light a cigarette (she only smoked if he offered her one, not sure if he approved or disapproved, she wanted his approval, not sharps or flats, she wanted it straight out, just like the chord of C).

▪

WYCK WALKED INTO THE bedroom of the Marie Antoinette, leaving Mary in the pink-and-white bathtub. He was dripping of perfume and bubbles and sugary water. The elegant room was filled with their clothes. Tabloids and weeklies lay on the table. There was a trayful of uneaten breakfast. Boxes of pralines and mints. Packages from Bendel's and Saks were open, and new clothes filled the hangers. A plethora of silken underwear and lingerie was draped over the chairs.

It was an idyll. A messy little heaven.

There was a knock on the door. No one was expected. Wyck slipped on a new robe and answered it.

Mary watched from the bathroom door, her tears bursting the bubbles of the L'Eau d'Etoile—airy bubbles, their perfume gone—as two detectives, hired by his father, shoved Wyck from the room and downstairs to a waiting car.

Chapter 7

■ AT 18 WEST FORTY-EIGHTH STREET, Mrs. Walton T. Elmsly, or Aunty, as she was known to the family, was overseeing the preparation of dinner—turtle soup, clams southside, French pancakes, and fruit compote. As she supervised the servants, she twisted her rings, musing to whoever was listening about resetting them or giving them away during one's lifetime to a cherished niece.

She heard Wyck brought into the apartment. A servant summoned her, and she went to William Hanover's study, which was filled with things of value saved through the centuries, divided up, passed down, only to be saved, divided up, and passed down again. There among the ancestral paintings, portraits of men with liver spots and almond faces, ladies with broken veins and eyes that stared boldly at those who dared to stare at them, was young Edward Wyck, white, shaken, overpowered by two detectives holding him firmly by his coatsleeves.

William Hanover sipped coffee from an antique cup. He dismissed the detectives and turned to Wyck. He recalled his heritage. Seventeenth-century Americans, French and

German Huguenots, people who made their fortune from sugar plantations, manipulating farms and factories, complete towns, whole islands. One boy would not mar this dignified history.

Aunty sat pensive. There was a certain pleasure in knowing one's opinion would not be asked.

▪

AT FIRST EVERYONE HAD coddled Wyck because of his bad vision and speech difficulty. His infirmities were almost cute when he was a baby boy, always by his mother's side, sleeping in a crib by her bed.

His mother was in bed a great deal. Her condition, described by the doctors as "chronic frailty," worsened each year and, in the fall of 1911, made them go down to Tuxedo Park, canceling their previous plans for travel. Peregrine Wyck (namesake of Peregrine White, the first child born on the *Mayflower,* the name passed on to her daughter, Wyck's sister) was a reedy Dutch beauty with the transparent skin of a white tulip, the granddaughter of a mayor of New York. She carried herself like his lead coach horse.

Because of William's insistence on social endurance, they entertained and traveled despite her growing physical weakness. His energy was boundless. Hers scarcely existed.

That last season they stayed at Dinsmore Cottage, a private hotel the Hanovers rented in its entirety. Her maid having gone down to the servants' quarters, Peregrine was alone. She had taken a bath and put on a silk dressing gown, and she sat at her dressing table, curling her hair for an evening party, when suddenly the alcohol lamp exploded, splattering burning liquid over her flimsy robe. She screamed for help. Begged for someone to come. But the servants' quarters were far away, the bedroom suites were empty. The smell of her burning hair and flesh surrounded her.

Frenzied and panicked, she threw herself on the bed, wrapping and rolling the bedspread around her, a writhing, stench-ridden torch trying to extinguish the flames.

Young Wyck was among those who finally heard her, watched unnoticed as she lay reeking and in shock for twelve hours as physicians worked over her. Young Wyck watched her die.

Wyck's sister, Peregrine, had been in the stables, putting a horse through its paces and flirting with the groom as only a thirteen-year-old girl can do. She had to be called and called again before she came into the house. The two older brothers, William Jr., a sophomore at Harvard, and T.C. Elmsly, preparing to enter Columbia, were observing the building of the Panama Canal with their uncle, T.C. Elmsly Hanover. When telegraphed, all three hurried for the train to take them to the funeral.

If William had been rigid, walling out feeling indiscriminately before his wife's death, he became worse, a satire of himself, when she died. She had softened him, but she had been the only monitor of that softness.

When Mrs. Walton T. Elmsly, sister-in-law of the children's late grandmother, herself a widow, asked William if there were anything she could do, he said, "Move in."

She did. She occupied his large New York apartments, leaving her own large apartments, bringing her cook and her driver and her maids. Childless, she did not take to being a mother, but she could schedule dancing lessons, hire and fire tutors, teach the children how to dress, instruct the cook, and make William's life comfortable enough so that he would never have to marry again. He became dependent on men's social clubs, belonging to four in the city (the Union, the Down Town, the Calumet, and the Tuxedo) and five for sporting (riding, badminton, yacht, hunt, and auto). A man of frozen habits, he alternated between them for meals and exercise, to discuss politics and war, and to ritualize the avoidance of his children.

▪

AUNTY'S EYES CAUGHT THE lighted candlestick on the mantle as she pulled the servant's cord, and the picture of Peregrine's charred and burning hair came into her vision. She shook as she asked the servant for a shawl and focused far away from the candle's flame, deep into the patterns on the paisley-lined ceiling. She would order tea.

"I . . . aaa . . . pppologize . . . ttt . . ." Wyck was trying to talk but he could not.

His father's face was paralyzed with rage, his eyes like glowing planets, glaring murderously at Wyck.

"You are a liar, a sneak, and an animal," William said. "You have no concern for those around you—or for this family, its reputation, or its fortune."

Wyck thought of Mary going home on the train, confused and crying. Was this the payment enacted for loving? As glorious as love had been, was this to be its equal in ungloriousness?

"What was in your head? You have ears and eyes. This girl, this Mary James, she knows you are rich. She doesn't care about you. She is an opportunist."

"I mmmm . . . met her . . ." Wyck began, but he could not continue. He had not, after all, met her chaperoned at a debutante party, or in the house of another good family. Small towns were way off limits, houses of strangers barred from visits.

"Does she coddle you, this whore? Does she tell you what you want to hear? Do you pay her cash or do you give her gifts? Oh, you have made us vulnerable. We must live guarded lives, and now here will come extortionists, blackmailers, publicizers—"

Saturn when displeased would eat his children. This was the look on Saturn's face before the meal began. William took a large breath like bellows fanning flames, then tipped a little on his toes like a loud and angry crane, tilted slightly to the side, and sat down. He tried to censor fury, passion deformed, emotions were despicable.

But he could not stay seated. "Lust. Uncontrollable, unquenchable, disorderly lust. Or was this an innocent try at boyhood, a jovial, gentlemanly sowing of wild oats?" He raised his voice. "Hanovers may not have wild oats. Their crop is punishment and the loss of freedom." He sighed loudly. "There is no sense in mincing words, I have minced enough of them for you, where have you shown that you loved or cared for me? Where have you earned my love?"

Wyck had stopped listening. He had lit upon a memory, years ago in Arizona at the Ranch School. He didn't know dogs well, never had one as a pet. Hanover dogs were for hunting, racing, gambling, breeding, guarding property, but not for fancy or for whim. ("A dog," his father said when he was little, "is not a companion. Man's best friend is man.")

There was a dog that lived in the cottage of the president, a corgi, brown and fluffy, an animal which tagged around, low-slung, like a walking slipper or a rug, his name was Mowby Dickie. Wyck was once in the kitchen, alone with this dog, it followed him, as though asking for something. Wyck did not think the dog wanted to relieve itself, having just come indoors, but he opened the door anyway. The dog did not move.

Wyck asked the animal out loud, "Do you want a drink of water?" No answer, so he filled a dish with water and gave it to the dog. The dog sniffed at it and walked back to Wyck, staring at him with pupilless eyes.

"No? Not that?" Wyck found some dog food in the larder, Say Please brand, and filled another bowl, putting it next to the water on the floor. The dog sniffed at it and walked back to Wyck's foot, making little whining sounds.

"All right," said Wyck, still talking out loud to the dog. He opened the school refrigerator and took out a lovely piece of filet mignon. Carefully, trembling from fear that someone would discover him, he chopped the steak into small pieces, put them in another dish, and set it on the floor. The dog ran up quickly to the steak. He sniffed at it. Then he walked back to Wyck's ankle, making louder sounds.

Confused, Wyck just sat down on the kitchen floor to study this Mowby Dickie, who, smiling a little dog smile, climbed into Wyck's lap and waved his tail and wiggled his little body. Wyck held him there, petting him, for that is what the dog wanted.

Wyck now stood before his father, as incapable as that

dog of talking, of asking for love—why was it so hard to say? Daddy, please sit down. Let me put my head in your lap. Please don't make me yet another bed of ice.

"From now on," William continued, his voice swollen and commanding, "you will not be left alone. These men will be your constant companions. Consider yourself a prisoner until you are of age."

"Ttt . . . ttt . . . two years?" asked Wyck.

"Exactly," said William. "You will travel. Where would you like to go?"

"Nnn . . . nowhhh . . . where," said Wyck.

William opened the door and called the detectives back into the room. "You, Hyland and Pearson, you're going to do some traveling. Where would you like to go?"

"San Francisco," said Mr. Hyland.

"Yosemite, sir, or Cuba," said Mr. Pearson.

"Fine," said William.

▪

WYCK WOULD WIRE MARY when he found out where he was heading (they never told him directly, but he overheard it), and she waited for those wires and would sit down and write her heart out, sending him pictures and poems, anything she could think of to keep him company and make him think of her. Her spelling and grammar were terrible, she knew, but she wrote him anyway. "I no you no what is stylish. I think this cottage is real tasteful don't you hon? When you have your own money you will make me real glad and give me lots of stylish things like other women what has men like you. I will get you a loyal hound when I have money. When I went to bed last night

I said my prayers to the dear God and I asked him to take care of you and I said thank you Lord for letting me meet Edward Wyck Hanover."

He would go to General Delivery, with the homeless and the nondescript, sneaking away from his "pals," as he called them. He wrote her of his travels, tried to make her see what he was seeing. "Panama, the Hotel Rivoli. Colon is the town and we are in a place built like a palace in Seville. We have a yard outside and I stood there last night and saw the stars and thought about how those were the same stars that were shining on you. And maybe you were looking up, then, at that same star that was shining and I was looking up, and we were together in that little star.

"The beach here is very clean and it's so soft when you step on it that it is like baby's talcum. The water is so bright and blue. Do you remember the blue dress we bought together? Well, the water here is just that shade of blue."

She wrote, tried to make him feel what she was feeling: "I was in Manhattan and I saw your house and I felt lonesome that I did not see you. A man such as yourself is terribly longed after. I bought a locket and when I close it your face and mine are pressed together. I love your ways like you love my ways."

Once he wrote that he was in Washington (Seattle) and she thought he was in Washington (D.C.). "You didn't phone. I am Crushed. So near. You have been a good peach but I do not want to fool with this love talk. I don't want pretty books and cards. It's you I want. You have always been good to me but on the up and up—what's the use of feeling this way if we never can be together?"

He wrote back in capital letters, underlined, "LOVE LIKE OURS WILL LAST FOREVER. MY FEELINGS HAVE NEVER BEEN GREATER, STRONGER, BROADER, DEEPER, AND MORE TO BE TRUSTED AND AS THE DAYS GO BY THEY WILL CONTINUE TO BE THE SAME."

Finally, he wrote of getting married. The cruelty of his father made him see things more clearly. The distance made him brave. "Our little secret," he called it.

She used that secret to keep her company when all her friends went dancing, which she didn't dare to do because it was a little crack, a chink in her decision to be faithful and to wait. "I have been true blue to you and lots of girls would not be and keep there word which I believe you did too but girls do not do what boys do and you will see that there are not to many girls that are loyal to their Sweethearts."

She knew he would come back. She knew they would get married, although Faye told her daily he was as much on the level as the Adirondacks, and she wrote, "My gang thinks you have left me forever, they say Mary, he is gone for good."

She went to live with Mrs. Hubbard as a nurse and housekeeper, which she thought would help pass the time. And she wrote, "I say to myself every night dear that you shall always be my Sweetheart and if you were mine and mine alone I would make sure that you were cared for. When I came to Mrs. Hubbards I felt so lonely for you because they have such a sweet little bedroom and a cozy place to sit together when they eat. They care for each other like we do and are so good to each other. And I thought we could be so cozy together in a dear little home just like two happy doves."

Weeks stretched into months and months into a year,

and she kept a scrapbook of the pretty scenic pamphlets and cards and views he sent her, she loved views, and she started buying thicker scrapbooks, and instead of sending roses and sweetpeas by delivery boy, he sent her everlasting flowers through the mail.

When she got tired of views and pictures from *Collier's,* she sent him pictures of herself, one in a slip, inscribed, "You can put your head on my pillow anytime."

He sent her an ad for silk underwear, "Love to get my hands on this."

She sent him a photo of a Kum-a-Part belt.

He sent Hawaiian love oil, "Moana Loa."

She begged him, "Please write something *interesting.*"

He wrote her a dirty letter.

She loved it and asked for more.

He wrote better and better letters.

She had to hide her scrapbook.

PART TWO

Chapter 8

■ "How BIRDS LOOK WHEN they are hopping in the shrubs and you can't see them but the leaves is moving up and down," Mary was saying to the snobbish modiste in New Rochelle, who understood her, for in 1923 a gown was more a descriptive phrase than a dressmaker's pattern. Her windows were full of designs—DINNER FOR TWO, LOVE ONLY ME, WAITING FOR HIM.

"Think it's too showy, honeybunch?" She turned to Wyck, his hair sleeked down Valentino style, his clothes perfectly chosen and tailored.

The modiste eyed them both. She shrank at his stutter and laughed at her lapses in English, but she thought them a handsome couple if they both kept their mouths shut.

"It's just perfect for Newport—evenings, of course," said the modiste.

"We're not much for society, is we, hon?" said Mary, sucking him with her lustrous brown eyes. " 'Specially since we got married."

Until now, "Honeybunch," as the modiste knew him,

had paid for everything in cash. On this particular day, however, the young man paid by check. The name he signed drew her attention. When they left, she went into the back room and called the local newspaper. It might be cruel to betray privacy, she told the editor who answered the phone, but celebrities belong to the public simply by being celebrities. And besides, the modiste said, we know they really *want* to be talked about.

▪

MARY WANTED TO MARRY him the day he came of age, but it took 117 days to convince him. Simply belonging to each other in each other's hearts, she said, reminding him of his letter, wasn't permanent enough. He could one day up and leave her (though he swore he wouldn't), just like a breeze off the water. And marriage is what happened if you loved each other, it's what you did. Love was not just talk or plans, it was acts. It was time for him to do love for her, no more putting it in the future. It was time for him to say he wanted her for life.

When Wyck was on his trip, Mrs. Hubbard had told her that she married her husband secretly because she was too young. Later on, when they announced it, no one cared because it was too late. People got over everything. Time healed, it really did.

Besides, no one in Felham cared. It was just his family that objected, and they didn't have to know. He could continue to work in his father's office (where he'd been given a job because it was easy for them to watch him). They could live together on weekends (weekdays he'd stay in the city) in an apartment taken out in her name.

Finally, Wyck came to ask her parents for formal permission to marry her.

"Go ahead," said her mom, "if you really love each other."

If they really loved each other? Their hearts were neon signs of love, they would be married lovers.

They told her parents it had to be secret from the Hanovers. The Lord works in mysterious ways, and Mom accepted this just as she had accepted Mary's story that Wyck was absent for two years because he went away to think things over. Now that he was spending so much time in Felham again, Mom believed his family must be reconciled to what was going on, or if they didn't know, they didn't care.

"Yet if it is hidden, something must be wrong," said her father.

"Just because it's secret doesn't mean it's bad. We'll tell them later. We'll tell them gentle and real slow," said Mary.

"Wyck is in a different world," said her Dad. "He should marry someone like himself."

"He would freeze at those altitudes," she told her father.

"If I were his dad, I'd be very angry," said George James.

"Oh, my dad's got so many other things to think about, he'll get over it really fast," said Wyck.

A shame, thought George. He had wanted a son very much. Too bad this father paid so little attention to the boy. Maybe George should start talking to him more. But he didn't like this secrecy business. There would be inevitable pain. Yet he liked the idea of breaking his daughter's heart a lot less.

"If you can't do it in church, I don't think you should do it at all," her father said. "But if you do it, once it's done, you must not leave her. There will be no turning back on this marriage."

"I won't want to turn back," Wyck said. "You know me. You've seen me. There is only one Mary for me. I don't want anything else. Just because it's a secret doesn't mean that I don't want her. But I can't walk away from my family, it would hurt my father, and Aunty. This is the only way to save their feelings too."

▪

IT HAD TAKEN HIM a while to get keen on this marriage, because, he said, it would not be the wonderful thing he wanted it to be. It wouldn't be anything like Peregrine's wedding at Saint Thomas's Church on Fifth Avenue in New York. A ceremony with sixteen bridesmaids (all debutantes and in the Social Register), all carrying American Beauty roses, Peregrine's hair studded with Japanese seed pearls and wearing her grandmother's lace, and throngs of relatives from England and France (both sides of the couple's family) crying to see Peregrine marry such a handsome young man (with three names), in that church, with limousines double-parked in front without getting tickets (which showed how important they all were politically).

It wouldn't be like that. He had told her when he came of age, "It will be lonely for you and me."

"But you and me can't be lonely," she said.

"Oh, Mary, I want to take you for my own. But I also

want you to have the things my sister has," he said.

"Is your sister happy?" Mary asked.

"No, not really," he said.

"Then I don't want those things," she said. "It's you and me, that's what I want."

They made a date with the mayor and signed the license, and the night before the marriage they sat in the James parlor, relieved by its traditions. They looked at the silver anniversary photos of her parents (crayon-touched by a Macy's artist). She said, "Let's make up death poems, you know, the kind they open only when you die."

They made up poems and exchanged them (each hoping the other would not die first).

As he left, she said, "And let's try to dream the same dream."

In the morning on the phone, he told her, "Do you know that I hate to sleep in the dark?" He could tell her anything.

"Really?" she said. "I hate to sleep alone, but that won't be a problem anymore."

"I dreamt there was a giant grizzly bear, drooling and matted, underneath my bed. It scared me at first, but then I could see it wasn't going to hurt me. But then ghosts suddenly came out of my closet, it's ghosts that scare me, they can't be killed. I woke up frightened."

"What did they look like?" she asked.

"Like the moon when it's out in daytime. And they made a murderous sound," he said.

"We didn't dream the same dream at all," she said.

"What did you dream?" he asked.

"I dreamt I was skating on a lake of glass, and when I looked down I could see fishes swimming under me and an ocean garden growing healthy, and it was like having all seasons at the same time, ice and warm."

▪

THE DUSK WAS A springtime in itself, you could hear lots of moving things, and smelling things, and blooms refusing to die even though it was late in the year, in fact, you could hear procreation, the heart of things exposed, duplicating themselves, promises of more to come. The cold made things grow in the night, kept them fresher, the world smelled like a florist's refrigerator, and the bright-colored flowers looked as though they wanted to fly right off their stalks.

What she wore to the mayor's office was so important that it barely mattered. She had chosen a traveling suit, appropriate for an office wedding, simple in style but made of thin white wool that looked like silver and lined with oyster silk. She had girdled her waist with satin braid and wound ribbons around the jasmine and gardenia and honeysuckle, all fragrant flowers, that made up her corsage. She wore a small hat that matched her suit, veiled with flowered lace that matched the blooms on her corsage. It was so very beautiful, and as she looked at it, tears formed, it was just so perfect.

When the first tear dropped, it made a streak upon her powder, and the thin line of kohl on her eye was thickened. She stood a moment, then ran into the bathroom and picked up a cake of Fairy Soap (the kind she had been using since she was a little girl). She washed the makeup off her face, rid it of artifice and paint, her beauty soft and timeless, a purity devoid of style. Wyck would see her clearly now, her birthday face, just plain old Mary as she was born. Even-eyed and honest-skinned, she went downstairs to join her groom.

▪

WHEN THE CLERK, WHO was acting as witness, put on the gramophone record of "Here Comes the Bride," he looked at her and thought, "I remember darker eyes and finer features, she's not such a piece of glamor after all."

What did he know?

The clerk and the mayor were sworn to secrecy, were even paid a little to keep their word, and Mr. and Mrs. Edward Wyck Hanover were legally married in the state of New York. The mayor and clerk sensed how much they loved each other, and wouldn't do a thing to stand in the way of real romance. A secret wedding. Romeo and Juliet. It was an honor to help love win out.

▪

OTHERS, HOWEVER, WERE NOT so gentle-hearted, for instance, the modiste who, a month after the wedding, called Harold T. Anthony of the *Standard Star* to tell him the scion of society's William Hanover had married the little daughter of a nothing-family in nothing-Felham. "It may be cruel to betray privacy," she told the editor, but he didn't think it was so cruel. His paper thrived on broken confidences, no muddied waters here, conscience was for amateur journalists and novelists. This story would sell a lot of papers. The wire services would certainly pick it up. "The irony is startling," he told the senior reporter standing in his office. "That boy's family, the Hanovers, founded Felham and New Rochelle. They're the family who donated that mammoth bell in City Hall Square."

The reporter knew the entire history of Westchester County, dating from the sixteenth century when Lord Fell, an English aristocrat, signed a treaty with the Indian chief Anhooke for 9,160 acres, including what became New Rochelle, the Felhams, Eastchester, Mount Vernon, the eastern Bronx, City Island, and various other islands.

In 1666, the next Fell sold 6,000 of those acres to the French Huguenots, who, by the grace of Queen Anne, were accepting asylum in the American colonies. In 1686, when the religious wars in England were at their height, Louis IV revoked the Edict of Nantes, which guaranteed religious protection. I have killed all Protestants, he reasoned—they no longer need protection.

In answer, 400,000 non-Catholics left Europe.

What family was among those to leave Europe and land in New York, purchasing property from Lord Fell, the very property upon which the *Standard Star* was housed? It was the clan of Jacob William Hanover, many times great-grandfather to Edward Wyck.

The bell that Anthony referred to, a relic from the Episcopal Church of the Redeemer, built in the seventeenth century but now outmoded by an automatic chime system, was dedicated to the city in 1884, along with a large contribution to the park fund and speeches by the self-appointed keepers of the Hanover legacy: We haven't forgotten, we will always remember Felham and New Rochelle, these children promised. We are your money. We are your power. We own New York. Why, the Hanovers are second only to the Astors as owners of Manhattan real estate. The Vanderbilts were Staten Island farmers when we were a proud old family.

The cynic in Anthony mocked the heady Hanover name.

Inscribed on that bell, now prominently placed on a pedestal that matched the stone of the old church building, were the words "In the memory of Jacob Hanover" and a quote from one of his letters written to his brethren still in Europe, "Come, for all things are ready."

"Well," quipped Anthony, "is he ready for this? I know the bride's father. George James. A Negro hack driver."

Chapter 9

■ THE TOP FLOOR OF the Coral Apartments, a newly built brick building on Huguenot Avenue in New Rochelle. Mary sat in their brand-new apartment, the cuckoo doesn't have a nest, and Mary felt like the cuckoo bird with half her clothes home and half of them here in the half-finished, half-furnished apartment.

Mary was repeating to herself the cure of the famous French doctor of autosuggestion, Emile Coué (recommended for overcoming every ailment from fear-of-dancing to cancer):

Every day
In every way
I will get better
And better
And better

She had just been subjected to the superior knowledge of Miss Eugenia Swift, New York decorator, who, having created a perfect little world for them, was loath to let them live in it, dropping in at least once a day and keeping Mary from moving in their private treasures—the bootleg liquor, the marriage manuals, the large collection of dinner menus she had so lovingly framed.

Still, Mary had to hand it to Miss Swift, who had urged all white, yet a white—the color of day—shifting subtly to creams and yellows as the sun rose and turning sapphire in the dusk, and when the moon shone the room went to pearls and grays like shivering sails in real moonlight.

Slicky-slicky and then some.

Miss Swift stressed harmonious elements as if even pastels would awaken one from the dream she had created; ferns and indoor palms were the only contrast in the room, rearranging light into lace, the little green bridges of shade echoing the patterns of the overcup oaks in the courtyard below. There was the thickest of rugs—spongy and plush—and stuffed furniture with extra cushions that were right in fashion. And those wondrously feminine things—an indoor gardening set, an incense burner that released exotic perfumes, a collection of Japanese candy boxes—all approved of by Miss Swift, who also insisted on Paderewski and Rachmaninoff for the reproducing piano, sighing heavily when she saw their large collection of jazz.

The issue today had been the bidet, which admittedly was Continental but also was embarrassing, and Miss Swift could not bear to face the manager the day the plumber came, ruing the day (she rued a lot) the bathroom ever came out of the closet. She cringed at the fact that Gillette was allowed to advertise in *Vogue,* armpit shaving having just come in. What would be next? Cupid's Domain? Not her, she'd die before she let that happen.

Mary rested from the marathon talk of Miss Swift and waited for Wyck to come back with her surprise. Would it be the purebred puppy (her wedding present) now boarded at the McCord Kennels until they finished moving in? Or cruise tickets? She dreamt of cruises, but Wyck's working in the city kept them from taking trips.

Though she was not flighty, Mary permitted herself daydreams, perfected them lovingly, trying them out in different situations and different locales. She had had so many dreams of what their life would be like when they were married that she had categorized them, made a list upon a piece of paper:

Vacation dreams
House dreams
Car dreams
Meal and drink dreams
Wardrobe dreams
Family dreams
Aging gracefully dreams
Being-rescued-from-illness dreams

Her favorite of these was being healed at Lourdes, but she couldn't imagine anything bad happening to her, so maybe they took her mother and father there to stop them from ever growing old.

In her cruise dreams she envisioned ships as big as downtown office buildings, nine-course meals on linen tablecloths, women who slept in dresses that cost more than his sister's wedding gown, and servants who spoke better English than she did.

But they never spoke to other people in her dreams,

strangers not perceived as enemies still were not perceived as friends, and Mary never urged Wyck to take her to social gatherings or introduce her to his friends.

She wasn't sure, anyway, that the rich have much fun. Maybe when she got old she would change her point of view and then she could take lessons on being acceptable. A woman advertised in the lobby of the Marie Antoinette: "Madame Louise. Charm. Poise. Personality analyzed. Correct social procedures taught personally or mailed."

For now, she and Wyck would keep by themselves.

So her surprise would not be a cruise or a party, but it might be another fifty-cent-a-mile ride in an open-cockpit airplane, an airplane which seemed like a tuna can, though the pilot swore that it was safer than an elevator. What could be more exciting than a plane ride? she wondered, and when she heard Wyck's key in the door she ran to meet him, a thank-you kiss forming on her lips.

Chapter 10

■ SHE WAS SURPRISED, INDEED. Behind Wyck, two men were pushing their way into the room, William Lawby, a reporter, and his partner, Everett Cubis, pulled down by cameras. They shouted mercilessly and shoved at Wyck (who was courteous by nature and, though he could win a fight, was unwilling to start one) as he tried to slam the door on them.

"Get the hhh . . . hell out of here," he yelled, alternately paling and flushing.

"Please," said Mary, unnerved and angry, seeing their muddy shoes and the ashes of Cubis's cigar about to fall on the rug.

Lawby, not used to watering flowers before he picked them, said directly to Mary, "The report of your being colored is very widespread."

Mary turned her back on him and found her way to a chair. Her legs were sticks about to break. This was a joke. A test. People couldn't act this way, there were rules.

"Get out of here," she said.

"Skin darkens when they get angry," said Lawby to Cubis so Mary could hear.

"Mr. Cubis is an excellent photographer, he will take any picture you wish, both you and Mr. Hanover," he said to Mary. And sideways to Cubis, "Eyes like an Ethiopian moon."

Mary shrieked at Lawby, "I don't want to be in the newspapers."

Lawby pulled out the *Standard Star,* its two-inch headline easy to read, "HANOVER SON MARRIES DAUGHTER OF A COLORED MAN."

Mary lost what little composure she had left, the tears started to flood from her eyes, "You'll pay dearly for this. We're not Negroes. Both my parents was born in England."

Cubis started snapping pictures.

"Come, honey," said Wyck, "ddd . . . dry your eyes and ttt . . . try to smile happy."

"It's nobody's business," said Mary. "We is in love and we got married."

"I'm the one to worry," said Wyck, and with all the force he could gather he pushed the reporters out into the corridor and shut the door on their fists, already clenched for pounding.

Wyck faced her squarely, dabbing her face with his handkerchief. "Well," he said, "is it true?"

Mary's thoughts were like unsettled glass in a kaleidoscope, not yet forming a design. She looked pleadingly into his eyes with such need and sadness that his own eyes filled with tears and she took his hankie and dabbed his face.

"Now, honey, let's not cry," she said. "I don't know anything about this."

She reached up and kissed him, her tongue exploding like lava from a live volcano, into his mouth and over his neck and chest, and she marveled that so much heat could live inside her as she reached to undo the buttons that followed the curve of her back, arcing her body as his hands reeled her in.

"You'll mess up your suit," she said as his pants hit the floor.

"I have another," he said.

But she was careful to fold her dress and remove her jewelry. "They're sharp," she said as she took the pins from her hair and rolled down her silk stockings, but he grabbed her to him, the stockings half unrolled, and they slid from the couch to the floor, his arms gently lowering her, guiding her so she would not hit the coffee table, and he fell on her body, which rose like a mountain pushing up from the ground until the lava of her mouth became the juices gushing between her legs and explosions rocked her body and his cock popped and came steaming.

▪

THEY LAY NAKED ON the floor, half aware of the pounding on the door and the noises in the hall, and as it grew louder they clung there coupled into one, beginning to fear the world outside, which was apparently threatening to drag them apart.

The loudest pounding was being done by Mr. Alan Stone, director of the Coral Apartments, and Mr. Henry Fellows, lawyer for the owner of the building, who was leaning on the buzzer. Having just chaired an emergency meeting in the apartment of the manager, these two men now had the task of asking Mrs. Hanover to surrender her lease "voluntarily."

The tenants at the meeting were paying a high rent for the privilege of living in the Coral, touted by its owners as "exclusive."

"What's the idea of admitting nonwhites into this building?" asked one of them.

"Pickaninny children running all over, why, those niggers breed like crazy," said another.

Mr. Stone did not defend his position. He had made an awful error. The lease was in her name clear and proper. She had brought a letter of recommendation from the mayor of New Rochelle, but he should have asked more questions. "We have all been betrayed," he said.

"Even if Mary Hanover passes for white herself," said one tenant, "she will have Negro friends and Negro relatives prancing through this building."

"We demand that you rip up that lease," said another.

"I can't quite demand that she rip it up," said Fellows, "but we certainly can ask her to terminate her stay."

The emergency meeting decided that Fellows and Stone should talk to the Hanovers and impress upon them how unpleasant it could be to live in a hostile atmosphere. They had gone directly to the top-floor apartments, but there was barely room for the two men as they walked along the hall full of journalists and cameramen (on their way down they would fire the doorman).

Fellows was still leaning on the buzzer when the door suddenly opened and Mary and Wyck dashed out of the apartment and ran for their car.

Chapter 11

■ THERE WERE MOBS OF reporters at the James house. Mary and Wyck followed the rules of stardom: Walk fast, avoid eye contact, don't let anyone touch you. Flashbulbs went off at a blinding pace. Reporters strained to see her face in the semidark. Photographers cursed the lack of light.

Mary was angered but back in control. Still, she could feel the moment changing, like when she went wading in the ocean and without any warning the sandy bottom disappeared, forcing her to swim.

A journalist barred the door, shouting, "You can't hide it, Mrs. Hanover. Your birth certificate, insurance papers, work records—your race is going to be listed on those."

"Your father is a naturalized citizen, so proof of his race is on file. We're getting the papers now. This is public information," said another reporter.

Mary bolted into the house, emerging in minutes, staggering under the weight of a huge gilt-framed tinted photograph of a dark-complexioned man with a curling mustache. "See," she cried, "that's my dear dad." Then she ran back and brought out a matching photograph of a woman. "Mom," she said, "this is my little mom." Her entire body was covered by the picture, and she swayed beneath its weight.

"Have you got any pictures of your grandparents—or couldn't they get the cameras into trees?"

"We're just as white as anybody," said Mary. She was about to fall apart, her eyes burning and her head spinning. The rules of grammar were beyond her. "And this thing never would have come out, only we was betrayed. You pay money for things to keep them quiet and then they come out," she said shrilly.

Wyck opened the door and pulled her inside.

Mary excused herself and went upstairs to her room with Sylvia, her older sister. Sylvia King (that was her married name), the oldest child of this immigrant family, may have been a prude, but she had a realness about her that the other girls, and even their mother, lacked. She had left home early, married, had a baby, and moved to another neighborhood. It seemed to Mary that Sylvia had always been a woman, while Mary was still a girl.

Mary closed the door tightly and put the whole weight of her life against it. "Is it true?" she asked.

"Didn't you know?" asked Sylvia.

"No, I didn't know. It might have crossed my mind or come up as a thought in my head, but it's like that time of twilight, you know, when it's not day and it's not night and you don't have to turn on the lights and you just sort of sit there. Then there's a moment when you know it's night. That just happened, that moment. When I was talking to those reporters. I suddenly knew something had changed."

"Nothing's really changed," said Sylvia.

"I was a different person talking."

"You're the same person, Mary," said Sylvia.

"Am I? Am I, Syl?" asked Mary as the tears started to come. The energy drained from her body, and she sat on her bed. The patterns in the bedspread seemed to press themselves into her, she felt indistinguishable from them, losing her separateness, weakened by each object in the room.

Mary always made up her own rules, thought Sylvia, didn't do what others did, and now, confused, whose example could she follow? But it was not the time to say I told you so. "Now what?" asked Sylvia, after all the silence she could endure.

"I don't know," said Mary. "I feel so lovable to him. It's just us two. I feel terribly scared."

She reached deeply into her oak hope chest, among silken underwear tied neatly in tissue paper with imported ribbons from a town north of Belgium whose name she couldn't pronounce, and pulled out a pint of bootleg whiskey. "I could finish the old bottle," she said plaintively. She took a very ungirlish slug and passed it to her sister.

She sat for a minute, then shook herself. "I feel more lively now. There's nothing they can do. Nobody, not all those straight-minded, gray-faced, blue-nosed, blue butts can stop us now. We're married. I'm going to kiss my sheik, and there isn't a thing, Syl, that anybody can do about it." She swallowed some Lavoris and went downstairs.

▪

HORDES OF REPORTERS SPENT the night in the Jameses' yard, sleeping in cars with the doors left ajar, blankets rolled out on the lawn, nodding in porch furniture, hoping to be awakened by the sight of the principal characters. The next day, ice-cold orange flip was hawked by vendors, and lines of cars, many with out-of-state license plates, drifted by the house. Spectators, some with tents and thermoses, camped out on the grass.

It was quiet within the house. Muslin had been put over the windows to keep reporters from shining flashlights through them. The only report from inside was from Faye who, as the *Daily Mirror* told it, came out to get the milk and morning paper, then defiantly stated, " 'This is some dirty trick. The whole thing is just jealousy. Women make me sick anyway. There are lots of girls around here who are sore because they didn't cop off a millionaire like my sister.' Brandishing a pail of water which she threatened to empty on the head of anyone who approached, she took the opportunity to tell the nation, 'My family has laid in enough groceries to last the winter and to feed the whole family during a siege of any length. And you can say for Wyck Hanover and the rest of us that we don't care what the Wops, the Swedes, the Jews, the Dutch, and the Irish say about us. We're as good as anybody and we didn't steal any Hanover millions.'

"At this juncture," the *Mirror* continued, "Albert 'Footsie' Fuller, not to be called 'Footsie' to his face, came out on the porch. He is an Italian gardener, stockily built, with a hat pulled down over his face. 'If youse guys don't keep away from here, I'll let the dog loose,' he growled, and made threatening motions with his fist."

"In a crisis," the report concluded, "the poor keep talking and the rich clam up."

▪

WYCK AND MARY TRIED to remain oblivious to the commotion outside. They spent the day barricaded in Mary's room, playing records on the Victrola and dancing, "Shake 'em out . . . Strut your stuff . . . Camel walk . . . Pull 'em down . . . Pickin' cherries . . ." They read the Dream Analysis column in the paper and the serials in *Collier's* and had long games of cards. In the evening, Faye snuck in a wine brick and they added water to it, getting drunk and making love in intimate silence.

"I love you, Mama," said Wyck.

"I love you, Papa," said Mary, but tears flowed readily. "A woman takes these things harder than a man," she said.

He was taking it pretty hard. He couldn't fall asleep that night, and when he did, he woke a moment later, feeling as though he had been hibernating.

Had they lied? Had they taken him for a fool like all the others in his life?

He had delighted in her skin color, weaving images of sultry Mary in his mind—wearing foreign costumes like the dolls he brought her, walking sheep at dawn through Mediterranean olive groves, pressing oil from cloves and reading palms from the back of Gypsy wagons. Her father was the color of the Spaniards he had seen in Cuba, brown and varnished, skin the tone of a rare and treasured violin, set off by white and plentiful hair.

His thoughts wriggled away from him like snakes.

He felt like walking out and leaving. But what if the stories were wrong, he would destroy the only love he'd known. And love was a reason unto itself, or so it seemed.

Fate hates unmixed emotions.

His thoughts went out like a match in a storm.

He dreamt of watchdogs turning on their masters; a trusted car which threw an axel while speeding down a hill; a rain like Noah's which threatened floods that would not stop.

He turned on the light, and it was twelve o'clock.

He woke Mary, and through a patch of woods in the back they made a midnight sortie to get air, stopping at the new Bar B Que stand on the highway, "A full meal on a single sandwich," just invented by an Ernestville butcher, and then they went back home and tried again to fall asleep.

▪

THE NEXT AFTERNOON ELIZABETH James urged bread and jelly on everyone as they sat down to tea. Wyck had never been with the entire family before (Sylvia and her husband, Robert, seldom came to visit, but they were here now with their little daughter, and Faye, and Footsie Fuller, a man's man). Their English jarred Wyck, Footsie like some kind of bouncer in a club, obnoxious, grating, "My neighbors was all kinds. I don't care if youse is colored—little raghead, eight ball, ring-tailed jazzbo," he teased Faye. "I've lived with Negroes all my life. No big deal if youse got any sense about you."

Mary felt like killing him.

Robert King drank his tea in silence, studying his daughter. He was glad they'd only had the one, and she was light-colored. He'd phoned his parents to ask if they wanted him to leave Sylvia, but they didn't want his child raised within a broken home. No, better to move to a new city. A butler in a home too much like William Hanover's, he knew he would be fired. But his surname was common, and Sylvia was light. They could keep it quiet. Mary's crime was trying to move upward in society. She was a fool. He was glad Sylvia had had no part in counseling her.

George James sat at the head of the table. He touched his long jaw, stroked it as though his face were bearded. His manner was English, his bearing impeccable, yet he was confused. "Why all this rage against the African?"

George knew little of his own ancestry. He was from the West Indies, but he had no family tree. He did not know the date of his birth. His mother had died when he was a child. His father had come to England in the king's army.

He himself had come to America as a butler to the former United States ambassador to Sweden. Then he worked in the New York Athletic Club and as a part-time cab driver, having sworn to change his status and searching for a job that would do so in this land of opportunity. At the club, lines were drawn quite sharply. The Negroes who worked there were very poor, the whites, who belonged to the club, were very rich with yachts and houses. The Negroes in Felham all lived on Mechanic Street in rented houses. They formed a kind of club of their own. These people had been slaves in Africa. George had little to talk to them about.

At work, he met a carpet manufacturer, David Gaston, who needed a man as superintendent for some buildings he owned. George was quickly raised to manager, collected rents, engaged workmen, kept the buildings neat and in working shape. Gaston was so impressed that he helped George save for his own building, introduced him to the bank manager, stood right by him and guaranteed the loan.

George's past was spotless, and his present was secure, for he had by now acquired ten thousand dollars' worth of Felham real estate. All of this he repeated to his family as a poultice to their fears.

"Since we don't know about our race," said Mrs. James, "and it seems so important to these people—why, look at all this fuss—maybe we should just say yes, we have some Negro blood. Get it over with, and then that will be that."

"You mean cop a guilty plea," said Footsie, laughing.

Sylvia got up, peeked out the window, and saw Leo Sanders with a group of men. Hard faces, and hands poised like spiders, twisting fingers like the ropes that were their brand. "It's the Klan," she screamed.

Mary saw a brick fly through the window, crash to the kitchen floor. Sylvia dived for her daughter, who started to gulp with fear.

"Oh God."

"They got ropes."

"Are there lots of them?"

"I'm scared."

"The window's broke."

"I'm cut. I'm bleeding from the glass."

"Oh my God. God help us."

"Hide real quick, let's hide."

"I think they're gone."

"Can you see them?"

"No, they're crouched down in the bushes."

"Call the police."

"The police are out there. They aren't doing anything."

"I'm going after them."

Footsie Fuller went out the door ready to strangle the men who threw the brick. George, the veins on his neck swollen, his eyes distended, pitched after him.

How old was her father? "Oh God, oh God," Mary murmured, and the cure of Dr. Coué came futilely to her lips. "Every day . . . in every way . . . oh God . . ."

Wyck reached down for the brick. There was a piece of paper wrapped around it with the skull and crossbones of the triple *K.*

Wyck was terrified.

Chapter 12

■ THE HANOVERS MET IN the office of the Hanover Realty Company to plan a stratagem for this family tragedy. (Coincidentally, William Hanover brandished a rental check from Theodore Dreiser, who was at that moment writing an imagined story, *An American Tragedy,* in the Hanover Garden Apartments in Washington Square.)

The principals were as follows: William Hanover; Aunty Walton T. Elmsly; William's older brother, T.C. Elmsly Hanover; his wife, Alice Clinton Fiske Hanover, and his son, William Hanover II; William Hanover, Jr., and his wife, Grace Anthony Hanover; William's daughter, Peregrine Wyck Hanover St. Paul Cosay, and her husband, Julien St. Paul Cosay.

There were five lawyers (not including T.C. Elmsly Hanover, William Hanover, or his son William Jr.), all offering their services for free: both Cox and Hyde, founding partners of their famous firm; Spottiswood D. Fowler, William's personal attorney; Alfred Clark, former ambassador to Germany; and a man by the name of Leon Tully, a full-time troubleshooter for the Hanover firm.

They were seated around a large oak conference table. William Sr. began the meeting with a sermon, quoting in part from a Thanksgiving speech by the bishop, Right Reverend Daniel Hanover of Philadelphia.

"Our name is based not on money or commercial gain, but on accomplishment, from colonial times to the present. Our ancestors filled the pulpits, commanded the armies, sat on the bench, and took part in the government of the Crown. They fought in the American Revolution, helped write the American Constitution, were members of the House and Senate and men of letters." Dramatically, he looked up from his paper, his eyes flooded but not allowed to flood over. "Are we going to give this proud old name to a nigger?"

Peregrine St. Paul Cosay was very much her father's daughter. She bragged about her strength of character, taking daily baths in a tub of ice cubes and racing champion whippets whose blood was as pure as hers. Tightly corseted, a Gibsonlike beauty with translucent skin, her hair rolled up like a giant pillow around her head, Peregrine sat strong in her chair, her feet firm on the bedrock of the Four Hundred—Daughters of the American Revolution, Society of Colonial Dames, the Junior League. She passed around notes that her friends had sent—messages of sympathy for her brother's marriage and an actual condolence card on her brother's social death.

"Come now, dear, calm down," said her husband, Julien, a banker, used to his wife's hysterics.

"Be quiet, Julien," Peregrine said sharply. Peregrine knew all about Negroes. The moon didn't shine in Harlem, and one of her friends swore there were cannibals there who ate pieces of each other in African tribal rituals.

Negro men had giant penises, and the women were all whores because they had inhuman sex needs. They looked like monkeys. Her brother's children would look like monkeys and have large penises.

And the crimes they committed. Grace Anthony had seen pictures of Negroes chained to stakes and gangs manacled together by the police in the South, where most Negroes lived. What horrible crimes had these Negroes committed to make white people punish them this way?

William Jr. read a poem from the *Afro-American,* a Maryland newspaper that had headlined and editorialized the marriage.

Mary had a little Wyck
His brain was light as snow
And everywhere that Mary went
For years he tried to go.

"Just give her money. Or have her arrested. Pay a judge. Kidnap him. Kill her," calmly recited Alice Clinton Fiske, T.C. Elmsly's wife.

"The legal process is good enough for the majority of people in this country," said T.C. "I know we can count on you to abide by it, too." T.C. was the family humanist. Recently he had read of a subway motorist who slowed his train to save a dog's life. He had ordered a medal struck on the motorman's behalf and would present one yearly. The more he knew about men, the more he liked dogs.

Mrs. Walton T. Elmsly, Aunty, interrupted with a radical thought. "Why not leave Wyck alone?" She understood him far better than anyone else. He was different from them, sought a new society. Let him live in it.

William Jr. spoke before his enraged father could. "Aunty, you don't understand. This girl cannot carry our name."

"It's not just our name, but our money and our jewels," said William Jr.'s wife, Grace. "Aunty, she's got that ruby ring, the one in the portrait on the Major's wall. Wyck gave it to her. What would Great-Grandmother Clinton say? Her ring on a black skin. A Negro at the Hanover table. Why, the servants will quit."

"We'll annul the marriage, and then, if they must, they can live together in some kind of sooty happiness," said William Jr.

"Possibly they haven't slept together and we can base annulment on that," said T.C. Elmsly.

Peregrine snickered.

"Miscegenation is illegal in half the states in the Union," said Alfred Clark.

"Oh, to live in California." Peregrine sighed.

"No possibility of a divorce?" asked William II.

William Sr. spoke commandingly. "A divorce isn't good enough. We will get an annulment. I'm sure we can find grounds for charging fraud."

"I want to point out to all of you that if we charge fraud, we can offer no money and there will be no settlement out of court. We will be accusing this young lady of a crime that goes beyond domestic dispute. Offering her money would provide her with an opportunity to accuse us of having conspired to perpetrate the fraud. We will have to have a public trial. We will then forfeit all rights to privacy," said Spottiswood D. Fowler.

"What kind of privacy do we have now? The *New York*

Times, which never exploits cases of this kind, has us on their front page, as do the *Herald* and the *World.* The tabloids have six-inch headlines, there is a comic strip running in the *Daily News* about Wyck and Mary, a contest to analyze the handwriting of George James to determine his race. Listen to this—*Socialite Duped by Negress. Blue Blood Weds Colored Girl. Society Stunned.*" Peregrine read from the stack of newspapers before her.

"*Laundress Takes Heir to the Cleaners,*" added T.C. Elmsly. "Why do men go to zoos?"

"And 'Milestones' from *Time* magazine," said William Jr. "*Married. Edward Wyck Hanover, twenty-one, son of William Hanover, Manhattan Real Estate magnate, to Miss Mary Beatrice James, twenty-six, daughter of one George James, New Rochelle cabman. . . . Mrs. Hanover is handsome of face, extremely dark of complexion. Mr. Hanover wears thick-lensed glasses, a sandy mustache, and a highly troubled expression.*"

"This is just the beginning," said Fowler.

"I have warned the servants to screen all calls and visitors. We've put a security guard on this building and made sure the doormen won't take bribes, and, William, have you thought of sleeping at a club?" said T.C. Elmsly.

"I can't face the men," said William, and his voice had a skipping falter in it, a slight weakness which he quickly corrected with deep breaths, like drafts which brightened up a flame.

Mr. Cox of Cox & Hyde fanned flames even higher when he said, "You know that trip out West he took?"

"What of it?" Tully asked.

"Did he write her any letters?"

"He did, the detectives said they couldn't stop him," said Tully.

"The saying is," said Alfred Clark, "Do write and fear no man. Don't write and fear no woman."

"Leon," said William Sr. to Leon Tully. "She must have written to him, too. Find those letters. Start a trace of her ancestry. And let's get Wyck away from her and set him to thinking straight so he will help us."

"I don't think he will help you," said Aunty.

"He will," said Tully. "There are professional ways to do this."

Chapter 13

■ LEON TULLY HIRED RAYMOND Stark, aide to Judge Sprockett in Brooklyn, thus gaining access to many of the court documents Tully felt he might need and, also, a process-server and a notary public. Because Stark worked for the courts, he could oil procedures which might take time if one had to depend on attorneys. And there was another bonus: Stark had the key to the summer home of his aunt in Belrose, Long Island, which was closed for the season. Having just received one thousand dollars as a preliminary cash fee, Stark was anxious to provide any and all services to Leon Tully and his cause.

Tully and Stark, attired as road workers, in workmen's caps with the brims pulled down, flannel jackets, and high, heavy-duty boots, walked through the crowd outside the James house. They had parked Stark's car up the road, and now, carrying tools, they made their way to the Jameses' back door.

Mrs. James, answering the door, paused to ask who had called for workmen, the pause giving Stark and Tully time to push their way into the kitchen.

Wyck immediately recognized Tully and tried to sneak out of the room, but Tully's loud voice paralyzed him with fear.

"Just hear me out," said Tully to Wyck and Mary and Elizabeth and George, who by now had come into the kitchen. "I have come to help. I'm on your side. I am afraid for you. The Klan has a watch on this house. They're building a cross to burn, planning a night raid if you don't get out."

He painted pictures for them: floggings, mobs, castration, lynchings. Mrs. James gasped. She looked tenderly at her possessions, her eyes caught the milk glass in the cabinet, and she took her Bible from the table, deciding to keep it with her at all times. She would sleep now with her shoes and her good coat next to the bed, one must be prepared, as the Bible said, sleep with your sandals near your feet and your loins loosely wrapped, for long gowns are not good for running.

Mary's heart was pounding. Things were out of control. Why couldn't she have her dreams the way other girls did? Why this chain of events—the press, the Klan, this short, hard man practically licking his chops at the punishment that was sure to be theirs—why had it begun? And Wyck looked sick, cowed, petrified by this emissary of his father (though the emissary denied he was such).

"If you really love Wyck, you'll want him to stay away from here until all this blows over," said Tully. "To show your love, you'll make him leave."

"I can't leave Mary," said Wyck.

"You must consider her safety, too," said Tully. "You can meet her secretly, we'll arrange it, just get out of here until this dies down. Look, this is Mr. Stark, who works for a court judge. He's going to prove Mary's not colored. We're getting the documents from Europe. All the press wants, all the Klan wants, is proof of her whiteness. You are white, aren't you, Mary?" he asked.

Mary nodded imperceptibly, a spider self-imprisoned in a web. She hadn't meant to say for sure that she was white.

"Well, then, there is nothing to be afraid of, is there? It won't take long. As soon as we leave, Mr. Stark can start."

Wyck looked around the room waiting for a signal. He knew he was in serious trouble, and he was sorting out what might come of it. He did not fear his family's abandoning him, he feared his own abandoning Mary, and his inadequacy, being thrown in the care of himself totally. He had learned not to trust himself, to rely upon the help of others. Now there was no one to help him.

It was Mary who broke the silence, aware of her family's terror and the fright in Wyck's eyes. He had lived a life of protection, he was unprotected now. "Go with Mr. Tully," she said. "We'll meet later. I'll hide, too, and leave my family out of this. When it's all died down, we'll go out West, like we said, or to Europe, far away, away where we can't be found."

▪

TULLY ARRANGED FOR HER to stay at the home of Mr. and Mrs. Rice in neighboring Mount Vernon. They were acquaintances, furniture dealers who had sold Wyck and Mary the chaise for their sun parlor in the Coral Apartments. No one would suspect she was hidden there.

Mrs. Rice was talky, social-climbing, exaggeratedly impressed with the Hanover money and social status, advising her to sue the papers when this was done for calling her colored. What a thing to say! It could ruin her reputation, and people wouldn't want to invite her to dinner or let her join clubs. When this was over, would Mary arrange a party for Mr. Hanover and his family and invite the Rices? Why, the Mount Vernon Ladies' Club, of which she had finally become a member (Mrs. Rice was Jewish and nothing in Mount Vernon came easily to her), would talk of nothing else.

As a result of Mrs. Rice's never-ending chatter, Mary stayed in her room a lot, looking out the window, waiting for Wyck to drive up and take her away. She watched the clouds as she did when she was a child, picking out heads, finding faces, upside-down pigs and cows whose eyes were the knots of climbing branches. But now she saw a fish with its mouth wide open, gasping for life, and a bird that looked like the fetus of a baby bird she had seen, prematurely outside of its shell in the grass, its eyes as big as its head, its legs like twigs curled around its beak, half-alive, still floating in a mucous liquid. She closed her eyes tight.

The phone rang. It was Wyck. He called her every few days from a phone booth in a drug or grocery store, away from Stark and Tully, for they had forbidden him to call.

▪

"AM I KKK . . . KIDNAPPED?" Wyck asked.

"Why, no," said Tully. "What a thought."

"Well, then, aaa . . . am I free to leave?" said Wyck.

"No," said Tully.

"Well, then, I am kkk . . . kidnapped," said Wyck. "You ddd . . . did this once before, but now it is a crime."

"Would you like to take me to court?" asked Tully, polite, patient, patronizing. "Of course you're free, but you don't really want to leave. You don't know what you want, do you? Your mind's a muddle. Would you like to go to court and argue that your mind is not a muddle?"

No, Wyck would not like to argue that in court.

He was in Belrose, Long Island, shut up with Leon Tully. Stark had gone to Europe, was tracing George's birth, writing daily on his progress or the lack of it with the Documents Office, railing against bureaucratic procedures and the slovenliness of nineteenth-century fact keeping. Transcript after transcript, file after file proved nothing. George James must be colored, said Stark, a white Englishman would have kept better records of himself. Why, this was proof of color in itself.

Wyck worried about what Stark would find. Having lost the steadying influence of consistent sex, the reassuring intimacy, the release of energy through Mary's body, he looked for security in physical exercise. He went to play a game of tennis, rode his bicycle until the sweat left a rim of salty white around his head. Every time he thought of Mary, he tried to turn the thought into activity—run till he could think of nothing but the pain in his calves, ride and jump a horse until the fear of falling off replaced the fear of losing love, exhaust himself until he was far too tired to long for her. It was an arduous process. He had a lot of energy. His bike tires were worn, and the mare flinched when she heard his steps.

▪

He remembered his father's horses, large animals that made a lot of noise. They pranced and reared and stomped, the trainer teaching them only to a certain point, forging a horse who would obey in a chase, but a horse whose spirit was not broken. They were, after all, horses made for sport.

As a child, he sat sometimes in his father's crotch, rocking aboard the heaving, bouncing horseflesh, jumping, splashing in streams, the smell of leather and sweat and shouts and whinnying all about him.

His father. A bull. A buck. A male, supreme and dominant. Lord of the Hunt. They always hunted at William's house, his hunts were hardest, fastest, most exciting in spite of fractures and concussions, and more than once, a horse had to be shot, a doctor called.

The kennel master would put bells on the twenty dogs. (Wyck was three when his brothers threw him in the kennel pen one night—he remembered the look of the dogs then, barking and fighting, howling, saliva dripping from their tongues and teeth.) At the sound of the leader's horn, the forest was filled with barking and chiming (all the hunters chasing some darting creature that later would be held up as a small piece of blood and fur), the sound of brush being crushed and creatures moving rapidly, birds hiding and then feeling unhidden again, forest mothers rushing to their young, and animals looking for forgotten holes and caves. The noise itself was like a fire. Like smoke warning of a holocaust. Intruders. Terrible danger. Danger so confident, it could announce itself.

William loved it, and Wyck hated it and found excuses to be weak and sick and stay by his mother, holding her warm and bony hand.

▪

HUNTING MEN SPEAK OF a sudden, unnerving fright called "buck ague"—a fear that a bigger, stronger, angry creature is hunting you. The anguished mate of a slaughtered deer, the mother of a bear cub about to strike. Wyck thought he had always had this ague, a fear that something was about to sweep down on him, to seek vengeance for whatever had happened on those hunts.

Could he ever get away from his childhood? It reminded him of the Chinese poet who died trying to run from the sound of his own footsteps.

There had been no contact with his family since the story broke. They had not tried to reach him. But they were there. In his head. And in the presence of Tully.

He wished Aunty would call. She might take his side, as she did when he'd gotten tongue-tied giving a toast at his sister's wedding. God, she had said, doesn't talk well either. But Aunty was churchgoing, temperate, a founder of the Women's Society for the Suppression of Vice. She didn't know about his life—breaking speed limits, dancing in public places with girls who smoked and drank. She wouldn't defend that side of him.

If his father were there now, he would ask, What on earth were you thinking when you married this girl? How could he make his father understand? It wasn't thought, Dad, it was feeling. I was feeling wonderful and I felt loved and the sex was great, Dad. He could just imagine saying that, his father clasping his heart in response as though struck by the men of his own Seventh Regiment.

The psychoanalysts and the habit doctors (as they called themselves at the Grove) tried to build in him the response of optimism, ambition, and curiosity. But Wyck was an inept pupil, couldn't get words out when people were in the room, the sentences were like rocks from an old slingshot, speech cramps, they called it, like a swimmer after lunch, doubled over in the water. Of course it was his father who scared him, and other people reminded him of his father. It did not take Sigmund Freud to figure that one out.

In his own opinion, Wyck did not need analysis. What he needed was a new dad. One who would approve of him and let him be. One who would not buy nurses, tutors, companions, boarding schools, cruises—all the socially acceptable ways for a rich man to reject his son.

Apparently his father was not going to call. Maybe he should write a letter of apology. Say he was sorry. Sorry for the trouble. Sorry he was born. Sorry he had tried to lead a double life, going to his father's office every day, listening to the secretary outline work his father had prepared, doing it slowly because if he worked fast there would only be more work to do, then calling Aunty to say he was not eating or sleeping at home because he had friends to visit, going back to the pleasures of Mary. He should have lived on his own money, he had inherited $400,000 when he came of age. He should have written his father then, sorry for you I was born, but glad for myself. I am going to open a supply store in New Rochelle. Or buy a garage. Or sell cars, which I know about, Dad.

Chapter 14

■ MARY TOOK THE LONG Island Railroad to Becker Beach, where she had reserved a room in a small hotel they had stayed in once before. Securing the room was a lonely chore, it made her feel too worldly, but she quickly said to the desk clerk, "My husband will be meeting me," and flashed her wedding ring.

It was off season, lonely, deserted, the hotels open only for the few residents who lived here year-round. Haze and fog sulking and drooping, made the sky the same color as the ocean, so no horizon was distinguishable, only an opaque and depressing wall of a view. The hotel's rattan deck chairs were all piled in a corner, and there was no place to sit outside. Her coat was not warm enough, she had tried to dress discreetly, fearing she would be recognized, or worse, that someone from the press or Klan would follow her. Anonymity was her only safety, and she longed to have it back. She realized now that the *Daily Mirror* stories, even the serials in *Collier's,* were for eavesdropping and snooping into other people's lives, and now people were doing the same into hers and she hated them for doing it and herself for having done it, and she vowed never to read the *Daily Mirror* again—or at least, if she read it, not to enjoy it.

She couldn't enjoy the money either, that was one thing she wanted to tell Wyck. The money had never been important, it was a kind of toy, a relish, side dish to their love. Let them have it back, even his grandmother's money. She could work. She had experience, she could take care of old people and young children and babies. And he could open a garage, he was so good with cars, or teach tennis, he was good at that, too. They could give back the money, it didn't matter to her, though she knew the Hanovers would not believe her. She also knew that all the goody-goody things she had done—being first in the Golden Rule Day essay, collecting the most for the East Asian Relief Fund, being picked by Harry Six, her banjo teacher, as the most helpful student in music school—nothing about her would help them to like her.

Yet she felt, somehow, that giving the money back would make them less angry. She wanted to give it up, give them everything—the Queen Anne bed, the satin drapes, the bidet. She knew whose face she would like to stick in that bidet—his sister's, Peregrine Hanover, the gladiator of the Four Hundred. Oh, she hated Peregrine, whose full-length portrait had made the November issue of *Vogue.*

But no time for anger now. She would give up her anger. She would give up the money. She would give up everything but Wyck. For what had begun as a rich man's game and a poor girl's dream had gone far beyond gaming and dreaming. It was something real and something strong. It was him and her. It was love.

▪

MARY, WAITING IN THE room, was restless. She opened the door and saw a cat go into the linen closet on the hall. She left the door open in case the phone should ring, and knelt down on the floor of the closet, petting the large cat, its fur a tortoise color like the back of an old beach boulder. She heard little sounds and moved the cat to one side, discovering tiny kittens sucking at the mother's tits, their slanted eyes squeezed shut, their little throats arched out as they sucked and pulled. Mary took a kitten and held it to her, the kitten still sucking air as though the sucking itself could bring the mother's titties back. No cries, no temper shown. Just the continued sucking of air. How long would it suck nothing but air?

The phone in her room rang, and she put the kitten back. Wyck was in the lobby. He wanted her to come downstairs.

He had aroused no suspicion in Tully or the maid when he rose early and, taking a mustard and cheese sandwich and a thermos of milk, bicycled off in his usual direction. But this time he parked his bike and boarded a train for the beach. Mary had pleaded with him to see her, it had been two weeks, but Tully had forbade it until Stark came back from Europe with proof that Mary was innocent. Tully was now talking about the possibility of a crime—fraud, lying about one's race, concealing ancestry, conspiring to mix blood. But Mary had begged to see him, she had to hold him and be held by him, she couldn't endure it any longer.

Wyck was pacing in the lobby and suggested coffee at a restaurant. It seemed as though some kind of realigning, re-creation of friendship, some seduction was necessary even though they were man and wife. A formalness had come between them. When they crossed the street to find a small café, it started to rain. Wyck opened his umbrella and it sprung a leak. The water started seeping through, and what would have been fun at a different time, even romantic, the water pursuing them like this and giving them a need to cling to each other, now made them cold and irritated.

"Let's have coffee in the room," said Wyck, and she agreed to end the walk.

Once in the room she could see how scared he was, how insecure, and how Tully and Stark and the separation had affected him. The wheel had turned in his thoughts. She was not innocent. She would have to prove her innocence to him.

"The lawyer we've been talking to, Mr. Claybourne, says it's going to be all right, honey, we have it figured out," said Mary. "No matter what my father is, he says I am legally white because my mother is white and that is the law in New York State."

Wyck paused, looked at the floor. "But that's not all right."

"Why?" asked Mary.

"Because you'd still be colored, Mary, it doesn't make you white in *my* eyes."

"Do I have to be white, Wyck, all white?" The horror

of it descended on her. "Why, our marriage license says I'm white."

"The clerk filled out the license," said Wyck. "And what the papers say, what the law says, doesn't matter. It's how I feel. And besides, I think you lied to me, Mary."

"I didn't lie. I didn't know. Is not knowing about something lying?"

"I'm afraid to trust you, Mary."

"Trust me," she said, moving closer to him, putting her arms around him, running her long, well-manicured nails down his back.

He responded, her touch connecting him with the source of all his wiring, and took her to him, but there was a new hesitation in his manner.

"Melt," she said, "like an Eskimo pie."

But he didn't laugh and he didn't melt, and she felt herself leading, aggressive, defeminized, and unwanted. As they started to undress it was she who pulled at his belt, not he who reached for the buttons on the back of her dress.

She slowed her movements, and his slowed even more.

His eyes caught hers, and she looked down and saw the bulge in his pants, his sex, his desire dissolving, dwindling, dissipating. "I ccc . . . can't do it with you anymore," he said. "We'll have to wait till I know. I jjj . . . just can't get it up."

He moved away from her.

Humiliated, she dressed. "I want to cry," she said. "I want to cry more than I ever have in my whole life. But I won't cry in front of you, Wyck Hanover, ever again."

She picked up her purse and walked out into the hall. Passing the linen closet, she opened the door and shut herself in with the kittens, let loose her tears until they had abated, and then listened to herself suck air.

Chapter 15

■ WYCK LEFT THE HOTEL and went back to Belrose, where he found Tully waiting. Stark was back from Europe, Wyck was to meet him at a subway station to sign some papers. "Let's get this over with. It's just another paper, you've been signing them all your life." Tully used the tactics of a dive-bombing bird, the discus player in a spin, his focus strong, impossible to interrupt, as he led Wyck toward the door. "Go ahead, meet Stark. Sign what he says to sign. We'll talk when you come back."

So, hurried to the train, late at night (why no chauffeur? why no limo?), no one to talk to, think with, heavy with the guilt of seeing Mary and failing her, Wyck went to meet with Stark.

The air inside the car was dense, no view, he was sleepy from the ride and irritated by the dim light of the station, when he saw a smiling Stark, holding legal papers in one hand and a blue Irish linen cravat in the other. The papers were turned down so only the signature line would show. Wyck had twinges of suspicion (beware of servants who bear gifts and coroners who hum), but he could not admit the possibility of betrayal, his imagination could not absorb any more bad news.

Anyway, she was still denying it, was working with her lawyers. These papers, whatever they were, would change nothing. He signed. And on his way back, he quickly wrote the note which she read in her living room. She had returned from Mrs. Rice's and was crying and holding the tear-stained papers asking for an annulment of their marriage and charging her with fraudulently concealing her race.

The note said: "Get a good lawyer, honeybunch."

The good lawyer was Lee Richards Thomas, a man in his forties, his face like a welcoming hand. A trial attorney with a reputation as a brilliant cross-examiner, he had been recommended to them by Felix Frankfurter of Harvard. Eccentric, a big-game hunter, a man who once made a rug with 18,000 Egyptian knots, he was patient, brilliant, and objective.

Frank Wheaton and Brian Wilkins, intense black leaders from the N.A.A.C.P., outsiders in the all-white neighborhood, had appeared at their door. She wanted them to go away, but her father asked them in. They said that Thomas had once been district attorney for Westchester County, but he quit because he wasn't paid enough. It was something that, on behalf of their organization, he was taking this case for free.

"Why?" asked Mary. Who were these people? Did she need the help of strangers? If she had lost his love, why win the trial? Here was a loss so large there was no winning.

"You are a symbol of outworn racial prejudice that the world no longer has a use for," said Wilkins.

"A symbol?" said Mary. "I'm not a symbol. I just went to bed one way and woke up another. I hate this feeling. I hate them. That goddamn Hanover family has made me a nigger."

The other lawyer had been wrong—her mother's race did not blot out her father's. Her mind spun to Leo Sanders and his group of men. The Klan had grown from only a few members in 1920 to 4½ million in 1923. She had paid no attention to them before. Now they seemed to identify what "Negro" meant—unwanted. Violently unwanted.

"You do have a choice, you know," said Wilkins, his hair like ebony chips, his coarse skin gleaming.

"What choice?" asked Mary.

"You could be a Negro," he said.

"Wyck Hanover can't love a Negro." She was crying deeply now, the tide was coming past her shoe. "And he wants me to win. And we is in love."

"You *are* in love," said Wilkins, correcting her English. "You talk like a nigger."

"Love," said Lee Richards Thomas, "is a feeling. Prejudice is a rock. You are going to be overpowered. Bullied. Stonewalled. Out-matched. Prayer won't help. Love won't help. Love is a feeling, and feelings give way. Get tough, Mary. This is an immovable, intractable force, and you've got to find another one to match it. And that will be the Law."

PART THREE

Chapter 16

■ SHE AWOKE THE MORNING of the trial, the night a tattered flag, the rising sun a baby's pink and luminescent belly swelling into view. She wanted to close her eyes and pull a Sleeping Beauty, awaken only to a prince's kiss.

The kiss was not forthcoming.

Mary opened her eyes in spite of herself. She smelled the ripening of apples and thought of Wyck, her life with him, their short-lived happiness. She had not heard from him in six long months, since his note and the annulment papers, and that alone, his firm resolve to wait it out, must be a lessening of his love. It was an object now, a thing upon a shelf, a piece of pottery or a photograph seen clearly from the outside. She was no longer able to feel it from within.

The trial itself was something to be gotten through, hurried, done with. It reminded her of missed steps and rocks unturned, animals left unfed, appointments missed and fruits left to die upon the tree. With sudden force she rose from her bed, reached for an atomizer bottle of perfume, and sprayed it directly into her nostrils. It stung. It was sharp and cold and the smell so strong it immediately plunged the memories of her old world back into her head.

▪

WHITE PLAINS, OCTOBER 1923, the Supreme Court of Westchester County. The excited voice of Alma Sioux Mayberry, a commentator for KBAY, Los Angeles, California, which had preempted all its programs for this special broadcast, narrated the action: "The courtroom is jammed to its doors with a crowd in which chambermaids and porters rub elbows with elite New York society. They have come from near and far—schoolgirls from White Plains High School, or Helen and Bootsie Connell, two middle-aged ladies who walked all day from Newbury, Connecticut, to hear this sensational trial. One flapper became hysterical when her autograph book was lost. A man broke his ankle running up the courtroom steps.

"Sweet young things, rolled of hose and powdered of nose, vie with barristers and members of the press for seats, as half a dozen guards bar the door. They have all come to hear Edward Wyck Hanover press his suit for annulment of his marriage, charging that his wife led him to believe she was white.

"Isaac Newton Wells, attorney for the prosecution, rises to make his opening statement. He claims that Mary James deliberately plotted to bring about the moral downfall of the young blue blood, five years her junior, a big overgrown kid trying to live up to his polka-dot tie and Valentino hairdo. Wells depicts his client as a weak, utterly unsophisticated young man, upon whom no woman had ever smiled until he encountered Mary James, a dusky vampire, a woman of many sweethearts.

"Isaac Newton Wells, alternately known as 'The Fox' and 'The Wrangler,' is seventy-one. He wears a skullcap over plentiful white hair and brandishes an ear horn. Wells, a senator from the state of New York, a teacher of many lawyers in the room, including the Honorable Mr. Lee Richards Thomas, Mary Hanover's lawyer, is a public figure in Westchester County, having once been a judge there.

"The jury—all men (the law does not allow women to sit on juries, declaring them to be too emotional)—listen seriously to Wells, noting the absence of young Edward Wyck Hanover, who has not yet appeared.

"Mary James Hanover arrived in a plaid coat with a fox fur collar and a cloche, and sits now in a light gray dress accented by a scarf with a silver trim moon pattern. The love light in the face of the cabman's daughter is a revelation. One sees why the starved heart of a pampered millionaire would find solace in the arms of such a girl, despite her menial station in life.

"Mary is surrounded by her family. Elizabeth James, her mother, is quick to frown or nod approval. George James, although he lacks a top hat, is dressed like a liveryman in Central Park. Her sisters are here, too, all of them sticking together now that the James family linens will be thrust into the same tub of suds that has already begun laundering the bedraggled Huguenot ruffles of the Hanovers of New York."

Mary sat on the hard court chair, her body numb, hoping her mind would follow suit, but it kept rolling. Maybe he won't come. Perhaps he's changed his mind. He won't go through with this. He's waiting now for me to meet him.

But he did appear. Wells almost finished with his speech, he entered with two bodyguards, and she could see that whatever wrestling in his soul or in a parlor with his father's agents was done. Haggard, costumed by his father's tailors, outwardly he looked distinguished, black jersey spats making him seem English, titled, from another culture. His overcoat was what men's fashion writers term quiet. He wore yellow chamois gloves carelessly unbuttoned, and a handsome malacca stick ornamented with a gold hoop lay loosely in his grasp. The other women swooned when they saw this model gentleman, society's injured lover, but Mary's breaths came slow and painful in her chest, her hopes all smashed, her heart put through a juicer.

As he walked to his seat, she leaned forward in her chair to gaze at him. A few weeks ago she had bragged to someone, and it had hit the papers, that when Wyck came into the courtroom he would run to her with outstretched arms. Mary waited for those arms to stretch out to her, but he would not even let his gaze slip in her direction. Instead he seated himself with his lawyers, Wells and Tully, and sat there steady like a horse with blinkers on, harnessed to stay right in line, an animal trussed to run a course, made blind to all except his private race.

▪

It was time for Lee Richards Thomas to begin his opening address. He rose and faced Judge David Morgan. "The defense counsel withdraws the previous denial as to the blood of the defendant and, for the purpose of the trial and to shorten the trial, admits the defendant has one-eighth colored blood."

He had told Mary he would make this announcement, but when it came, she hid her face behind a silken hankie, pellets of sweat on her forehead, shocked by the public recognition of what was now a fact. Her father's mother was one-half Negro. Her race determined, she was barred from private clubs, the Social Register, and better southern bathrooms. She was connected now to Little Evas chased by guard dogs, and Aunt Jemimas, stomachs resting on their knees—a race of moaning, praying, servile women.

Thomas had said her case must rest on her denial of fraud. She had not stated that she was white. Had Wyck asked her, she might have said, I do not really know my race. Had he asked her father, George James might have said, Yes, I could have some colored blood. This must be their argument.

"But if I say I am Negro," Mary had protested in a meeting with Thomas, "they will say that I was passing. They will say I knew and lied. That we all knew and lied and went to white schools and a white church and pretended we were white."

"Race is not an opportunity for confession," Thomas had said. "Why admit to being Negro? Who admits to being white? To being Spanish, German, French, or Asian? There is no law that says you must. 'Passing' is a racist's term."

"But they can't prove I'm Negro."

"Your father has signed papers saying his blood is mixed. He sees no problem in being one-fourth Negro.

You must adopt this view, Mary, you must rise above yourself."

And so, destroyed by lawyer's logic, she finally said, Do what you have to do, it doesn't matter, you don't need my brain, I'm just the victim here, and help me, help me, I have to trust you because I got myself in trouble, yes I did—but still the words, hearing them now, they were like bullets, yes, she was being killed, the old Mary was being murdered by her very good friends, but what was so bad about that old Mary, that pretrial Mary, what was so bad about her anyway?

▪

To WYCK THE FACT that she was Negro came as a betrayal, unexpected (a dentist pulled a tooth and said "Surprise," a trusted doctor gave a wrong-type blood transfusion), his body couldn't absorb it, it came out of nowhere, this admission, this confession, without his lawyers having had to lift a hand.

He had walked into the courtroom hoping she would win the trial. He hoped her lawyers had a better case than his, her victory really his, really theirs. His leaving her and going with Tully had been *her* idea, she had told him he should go. She had planned the wedding, chosen their apartment, she would find a way to keep them together, so he thought, and he had fantasized the moment when she won. He even thought while dressing that she would like this Continental look. He had not looked at her, saving her face (stardust made manifest, her pupils tinted like the bottom of a stream, a gaze that could find deer tracks in a pond) for that big embrace when they would leave the courtroom arm in arm.

He had been certain that nothing as beautiful as they had could ever get ugly; that nothing as warm as they were could ever grow cold; that nothing as natural as what had happened to them could ever go wrong. He had thought they were like two eyes—one could not move without the other.

But now, hearing she had Negro blood was like a stone thrown high in the air, destined to fall of its own weight, not like a bird that when upward thrust would take wing.

This morning he had dressed himself in his usual way, putting on a shirt, trying it with a tie, then finding a pair of trousers, and if they didn't work, trying another shirt, another tie. He always had a lot of clothes spread on his bed before he looked right. He couldn't remember combinations, had to make them up each time, hit and miss, by instinct, put it all together first to see if it looked good. Mary had been able to plan, see combinations. For her, difficult things were just simple.

But now it hadn't worked. His Mary had been wrong. Or she had lied.

And he, assuming she was Spanish, white, or Latin, then finding she was not—assuming this, assuming that—this was no way to live.

Was his father right? Was there nothing in which the sour would not override the sweet, an enemy in every box of Cracker Jacks, all houses built of matchsticks, a trap in each hello?

He wanted so to look at her. Just a glance. A glint, a graze, a ricochet. But his feelings might be shanghaied once again. And now the trial was really over, anyway, she had been mistaken or lied, what was the difference? The marriage would be annuled, he would go home.

But where was home? He had lived for six months in Belrose with Tully and Stark. They had come to White Plains for the trial and were now staying in a suite at the Gramaton Hotel near the courthouse. They ate in the dining room, discussing the freshness of the rolls, the staleness of the air. Their rooms smelled of small-town disinfectants, the chef used canned sauces trying to imitate New York French restaurants, Wyck was whisked around in unpretentious cars by nonuniformed chauffeurs. Eventually he would have to see his father, who had said he would not see him until he won the trial.

So he sat, now feeling like an old Victorian doll, his lids on hinges, his knees on rusted hooks, his organs cracked like dried balloons. Like an antique child's toy seated in the window of a moving train, the scenery changed and shifted necessarily, while he sat and, helpless, watched the trial move on.

▪

AFTER THE ANNOUNCEMENT OF her race the court was stilled, reporters returned from calling city desks, Lee Richards Thomas took up his opening oration. He called attention to the fact that Edward Wyck Hanover had been late. "Was he asked to be late by Wells so that he would not hear himself described as a brain-tied, weakly retardate? Yes, indeed, he was kept from this room on purpose. Why, this young man, according to his lawyer, is bughouse, his mental machinery hasn't been going around for years. This boy, descendant of a long and ancient line, stuttered and went to a school for slow children and was so befuddled he didn't know what it meant when she asked him to come to her house. And she duped this stammering nut, and now that nut should be released from his wedding vows, no matter what it is to cost this girl. Mr. Wells wants you to believe that Papa's son was seduced.

"But it is Papa, not his boy, who conceived this. William Hanover's millions are behind this plot to crush a concededly humble family's attempt to save what they regard as an honorable name."

Wyck sat motionless through this speech, staring ahead, an apple lopped off a golden tree. Mary dry-sobbed, stared at her shoes, prayed deeply for a release, a miracle that would unbolt the courtroom door, put the key into the car ignition, speed her off into a future that did not have this past.

▪

Isaac newton wells, summoning all the majesty the bench demands, stood up. His black cape like hawk's wings encircling prey, he called his first witness to the stand—Frank T. Ekhert, who, once duly sworn, said he was clerk in the County Office of Immigration, trying to be calm but so unnerved he drooled a little as he talked.

"Does this testimony have any bearing on color?" asked Thomas.

"Yes," Wells answered. "This is the father's oath."

"We have already conceded the matter of color," said Thomas. "Just put it in evidence."

But Wells insisted that Ekhert read the document he was holding—"I, George James, colored man, do declare an oath that is bona fide in my intention to become a citizen of the United States . . ."—giving reality to the public declaration of her race. And after Ekhert came another witness who read Mary's birth certificate, on which her color was called mixed, and then her marriage license, where Mary's race was listed as white (thank God the clerk had done it, she could have written white herself and weakened her own case).

Then Raymond Stark was called to the stand. Sitting next to Wyck, he faded like the lawn a peacock stands on, but now, on the stand by himself, he acquired a vicious, military look. He told how he had gone abroad to look for George James's birth certificate and his wedding license but found neither. He had taken a separate trip later, he said, to visit Elizabeth James's parents (who, he added, were illiterate and so could not be reached by writing), but returned empty-handed. He could report only that there were no papers on file in England.

Mary had thought there would be one at least, what a dumbfounder, no proof at all, just her father's volunteering, yes, he had always known that somewhere in his mother's line there was a Negro. Like volunteering, she thought, for a suicide mission. Thomas had persuaded them to declare their color when, in fact, they could still deny it if they really wished, yet they had agreed at his urging to wear this crown of thorns, this thistle bridle.

▪

THESE PAPERS NOW SUBMITTED into evidence, Isaac Newton Wells called Mademoiselle Francine Duclos to the stand. She was wearing basic black with jewelry given to her by past employers. Without a family, her memories of other people's pasts had become stronger than her own. She had come forth voluntarily, as Edward Wyck Hanover's governess around the time his mother died, to speak on his behalf.

"One of my jobs," said Mlle. Duclos, "was to teach him French, but it was very difficult on account of that terrible impediment he had in his speech."

"Did you notice anything during those four years about Edward Hanover's quickness of mind?" asked Wells.

"Your Honor, that we object to as improper and incompetent," said Thomas.

The judge instructed Mlle. Duclos on how to answer Wells's question. "There is a rule of law about such testimony as yours. A physician may testify in general and give his opinion, but a lay person such as you or I must state only the facts. You must try to recall any particular incident which would illustrate your point. Can you do so?"

"There were so many I can't remember," said Mlle. Duclos.

"That we object to as incompetent and improper," Thomas said again.

"I believe Mr. Wells is laying a foundation," said the judge.

"I cannot be expected to read his mind," said Thomas.

"Let me explain it to you," said Wells. "I do not claim the boy is a lunatic. I am simply saying that he was backward in his mental development when he was nine years of age. That has some bearing on the future probability of fraud."

"I believe you are right," said the judge. "The principals may have been on terms of inequality. Not socially, but mentally. Mademoiselle Duclos, can you now recall an illustration of Mr. Hanover's alleged mental backwardness?"

"For instance," said the governess, "I might give him something to learn and he would learn it perfectly well. Then I would ask him perhaps an hour or two afterward, and he would have forgotten it entirely."

"Did this happen repeatedly?" asked Wells.

"Yes," said Mlle. Duclos. She proved to have an excellent memory, reciting incident after incident of crying spells and moodiness as well as verbs that strayed and conjugations that were lost.

When Wells was done, Thomas took up the cross-examination. "You have tutored other Americans in French, have you not?" he asked the lady.

"Yes, a great many," she said, her distaste for Thomas surfacing in a kind of tick, a moving flinch that pinched her cheek.

"And you find that we Americans have some difficulty with French?" asked Thomas.

"Not so much as the English have," said Mlle. Duclos.

"I am not talking about the English," said Thomas.

"I think Americans are very quick in learning French—most of them," said Mlle. Duclos.

"Well, there is some difficulty in teaching a chap who can't use his tongue freely," said Thomas.

"Not always," said Mlle. Duclos. "It depends very much on the memory and power of the will."

"You recognize, don't you, that it is pretty nearly impossible to teach French to a man who stutters?" asked Thomas.

"No," said Mlle. Duclos. "I believe he understood French and learned it quite well when I was there."

"A person can stutter in French as well as in English?" said Thomas.

"Just as well," said Mlle. Duclos.

"Thank you, that is all, mademoiselle," said Thomas.

▪

The next witness was Justin Thresher, a small and gloomy man garbed by the church.

"What is your profession?" asked Wells.

"I am a chaplain and a clergyman," he said.

"Were you at one time pastor for the Hanover family? At the church to which they belonged?" asked Wells.

"Yes sir," said Thresher.

"Did you know, from your acquaintance with the family, who was the Hanovers' founder in this country?" asked Wells.

"Your Honor, Mr. Wells, we are not claiming here that the plaintiff has anything but white blood in his veins," Lee Richards Thomas interrupted.

"I would like the court record to show that the plaintiff, Edward Hanover, is a direct descendant of Jacob Hanover, French Huguenot, one of the original settlers of New Rochelle," said Mr. Wells.

"If you will state it as a fact, I will concede it," said Thomas.

"I will show it to you in Bolton's history," said Wells. He continued with Thresher, "Do you remember the death of Mrs. Hanover, plaintiff's mother?"

"I was one of those who officiated at her funeral," said Thresher.

"Did the children of Mr. and Mrs. William Hanover attend your Sunday School, and what were their names?"

"Well, there was a daughter, Peregrine, and Edward and two other sons, William, and T.C. Elmsly the second," said Thresher.

"The last son you mentioned, T.C. Elmsly the second, is he living?" asked Wells.

Thomas rose quickly, "That is objected to as immaterial."

"I wanted to show that he was killed overseas in France in the war," said Wells.

"What difference does that make?" asked Thomas.

"It shows something of the blood," said Wells.

"Do you mean that an annulment could be granted on the brother's bravery?" asked Thomas.

"Your theory seems to be that an annulment must be granted on one individual fact out of a thousand facts in a case," said Wells.

"You are putting this in only to catch the sympathy of the jury," said Thomas.

"Mr. Thomas, either make the objection or withdraw it," said Judge Morgan.

"I object, it should be stricken from the record," said Thomas.

"That is denied," said the judge.

"Now, then, Reverend, please turn to the difficulty young Edward Hanover had in speaking. What did you notice as to his mental operations?" said Wells.

"Just a moment," objected Thomas. "This gentleman is not qualified to state plaintiff's mental operations."

"State facts only," the judge instructed.

"Well, for instance, there were contests in Sunday School for learning certain things, such as verses during Lent and so forth. Edward was always one of those who failed. He never succeeded in learning anything. In fact, his graduation had to be held in private because he couldn't make a little sermon in front of the assembled church."

On cross-examination, Thomas asked the witness, "You made a special effort to teach this boy, did you, sir?"

"Yes, I did," he said.

"Reverend Thresher, I can still remember my own Sunday School days. Have you ever observed a boy who was slow in Bible study, but awfully fast at baseball?" said Thomas.

"Decidedly," said Thresher.

"Have you ever observed a boy who was a little slow at memorizing sermons but worked very fast when he was making love?" asked Thomas.

"I have," said Dr. Thresher.

"That is all," said Thomas. "Thank you."

▪

THE NEXT WITNESS WELLS called to the stand was a dignified man who identified himself as L. Pierce Woods.

"What is your profession?" asked Wells.

"I am a doctor," said Woods.

"Have you any specialty in your practice?" asked Wells.

"Yes, I do," said Woods. "It is the treatment of nervous and mental disorders."

"Are you connected with any institutions devoted to this treatment?"

"I am consulting physician to the Manhattan State Hospital, the Kings Park State Hospital, the Central Islip State Hospital, Letchworth Village for mental defectives, and Randall's Island Institution for feebleminded children. I am also consulting neurologist to the Craig Colony for epileptics and an advisory consultant to the Board of Education in New York."

"How did you come to know the plaintiff?" asked Wells.

"He was a private patient of mine," said the doctor. "I recommended that he be sent to the Grove School."

"Now, it is your practice, is it not, to make records of your cases?"

"Yes."

"Will you read from your records on Edward Hanover for February 1920," said Wells.

The doctor read, "February 14, 1920. The boy arrived early Monday morning with his father. There is a present sense of fear and an apparent lack of affect."

"I want to know what the word 'affect' means," Wells interrupted.

"It is emotional response. An emotionally healthy person has a great deal of affect—attitudes and feelings. In young Wyck, as he was nicknamed, it was what we call effaced—wiped out, erased." Dr. Woods resumed reading, "His constitution reflects sluggishness, so we have prescribed a swimming program and a regimen of Hormotone. He is shy and diffident in our analytic work, but he can remember details from his past. He actually recalls falling out of a baby carriage, cutting his head on the sidewalk, and being carried into a drugstore."

"Then you concluded that he should be in some sort of treatment," asked Wells. "It was your diagnosis that Wyck, if I may, had something more wrong with him than a speech difficulty."

"Most definitely," said the doctor. "Edward Wyck Hanover was suffering from an arrested mourning reaction. He had a defensive denial of the loss of his mother coupled with a crippling guilt due to superego conflicts over the aggression he felt toward the loss object—psychoanalysis was indicated."

Mary listened. Did she understand the doctor right? Had Wyck's mind been damaged by his mother's death? Were his emotions not like normal people's? Was she then to blame for marrying him? She felt lost without guidebooks, stranded like a navigator mapless on a foreign sea. It was as if someone had up and taken the North Star, stolen God's very compass, Polaris, no longer available to travelers, hikers, and people just lost in the dark—good Old Dependable, sure and reliable, it had disappeared, maybe sitting now in somebody's pocket, glittering away, or perhaps captive in a five-cent locker in a jazz dancehall.

Chapter 17

■ Eddy rose sat up straight on the courtroom bench. He had come to testify against Mary. His collar broad, his hair cut square and proper, he was now a fireman, still full of words like "duty" and "good sport" and "fair play." He had come to say he had never asked her to marry him, they weren't engaged, and she, in telling Wyck they were, had lied to him. Besides, Eddy knew she wasn't pure "American." Prince Boswell, from Felham, a veteran in a black regiment called the Buffalos, had told him Mary's father was colored—and that was why he never called on his return.

But now Eddy looked at Mary there, against all those people, she was sitting so bravely, holding in her emotions, not even crying, not letting them take anything away from her that was hers—after all, she had a right to that money and that name if he had married her, he hadn't thought of that before. Eddy Rose looked at her and he felt sick, his hand went to his mouth and he rushed from the courtroom to the lavatory. When he was interviewed afterward by the press, he said he came to speak against her but, now seeing her, he wished her all the luck in the world. "She is a wonderful girl and she came to me when I was the most scared fellow in the world and she did, she made it better."

He waited for the next recess and went up to her. "How are you, Mary?"

"Playing the highs and the lows," she said.

"I want to say I'm sorry," he said. "You're a wonderful girl, Mary, you really are. I only came, well, I thought you were trying to get away with something, but I see you're not, Mary. You're only fighting for what's yours. They're the ones who are wrong."

It should have made her feel better, but it didn't, this awkward man coming out of her past, holding his feelings in his hands like water when there is no cup. He was making her think and making her feel and the time for that was later. She was locked up now, locked up in the trial like a fairy-tale creature cursed to live in the suit of a frog, and she could only shake her head and hold her tears inside and push her way back into the courtroom.

▪

RECOVERING FROM THE LOSS of a good witness (Rose would have helped, but they would do just fine without him), Isaac Newton Wells took the time to bring on Mrs. Rice. She had the look of someone good at cleaning fish and training dogs. She cringed openly as she walked to the stand, the crowd was one-third Negro (the room divided as for a wedding, one side for the bride and one side for the groom). The darkies looked to her like they were outfitted for the race track on a Saturday night. She herself had dressed appropriately, wearing a woolen frock imprinted with tiger lilies and a smart felt hat wound about with purple tulle.

Thomas watched her. She could have been in the audience at the Coliseum, watching the gladiators cheering a death, no matter what the price, the only point was winning.

"It's just the principle that counts," she said. "Those Jameses want us to believe they never talked about their race. How could they not discuss it? They're lying, I know. The Negroes in this town all live over on Mechanic Street, they're poor and slow. So her family studied some, put on a real good show. Mr. James here looks just like an Englishman with jaundice."

She spoke in falls of words that the judge did not bother to stop, glared right at Mary, "This girl put one over on all of us," she said, darting sympathetic looks at Wyck, who was chain-smoking, dashing cigarettes to the floor and crushing them with his heel.

"When did you first meet Mary Hanover?" Wells asked.

"Well, when Mr. Rice told me that one of *the* Hanovers had settled in New Rochelle and needed furniture, I thought we might have something for them. But I was surprised that they moved here. We are society people ourselves, and we would rather live near Wall Street.

"The four of us got friendly and we arranged to see a theater piece. We drove to New York to see the Four Marx Brothers in *I'll Say She Is,* and we went out to dinner first."

"Now, at the restaurant," said Wells, "what happened?"

"Well, I presumed we were going to a hotel for supper, which perhaps we would have, had they not been delayed, but Edward chose a charming Chinese place instead. I had on a sleeveless evening gown and I asked her at the table, 'Why do you have on a long-sleeved dress?' She said, 'I generally wear long sleeves because my complexion is dark. You know, Mrs. Rice, we are of Spanish descent.' "

"Now then, madame," said Wells, "I want to pass along to the time after her husband had left her. Did she come to your house then?"

"Well, at the time I was at my sister's house and they couldn't get me on the phone, but eventually my husband came down and said, 'Maude, have you any objections to Mrs. Hanover coming to the house for dinner?' "

"How long did she stay?" said Wells.

"Two weeks."

"Now, during that period of time did she say anything to you regarding color?"

"She did. She said that if it took every penny her father had in the world, she was going to sue the newspapers for daring to call her Negro. And I thought, here is this defenseless girl in love with a millionaire's son and it's so unfair, the papers want to destroy something so charming."

"Did Mary say anything else about her race?" asked Wells.

"She said that Edward would rather marry an Eskimo than a Negress, and he would stick by her."

Wells sat down and Thomas got up. He asked her, "Your voice is pitched quite high, isn't it? I am asking that for the purposes of the record."

"If you were in my place, your voice would be even higher," said Mrs. Rice.

"Do you like Mary?" Thomas asked.

"I did, very much," said Mrs. Rice.

"Do you like Mary?" he asked again.

"No," she said.

"Do you have a sort of hatred for Mary?" asked Thomas.

"No, I have never borne hatred in my life," she said.

"You just dislike her."

"Yes."

"When did you begin to dislike her? The date please."

"I began to dislike her when I saw in the papers that she admitted she is a colored girl."

"You dislike her because she is a colored girl?"

"No, because she deceived me."

"You would not have a colored girl in your house?"

"Yes, I would, but I would like to know it. I defied the whole world for her. She said that she was white, and then her whole family had a good laugh at me. I was at my sister's store when the story came out in the paper, and I was pointed at by everybody and laughed at in business for believing she was white."

"Then you have good reason to come here and testify against Mary," said Thomas.

The sight of Wyck was his most eloquent defense. Called to the stand by Wells, his sadness, his despair, his unease with his own controversial, overwhelming feelings, made him shaky, caused him to rock dazedly in his chair. His appearance gave credence to Wells's contention that he was unfit to make decisions, bait for other wills and uses turned against his benefit.

He was barely able to take the oath, almost soundlessly stammered out, "I ddd . . . do."

Wells treated him like an invalid.

Mary's eyes fastened on Wyck's face, and she remembered reading about an experiment in psychology, and so she stared, I will make you look at me, I will make you look at me.

But Wyck looked only at Wells, who was asking his name, his age, the details of his first meeting with Mary.

"Won't you tell us, as briefly as you can, when you first met Mary James? I might ask you, did you meet the defendant first, or did you meet one of her sisters first?" asked Wells.

"I mm . . . met Faye, her sister," Wyck said. "We hhh . . . had trouble with the car, three of us had gone out driving, and she hailed us from the sss . . . sidewalk, and Carl drove her over to Felham."

"Who was Carl?"

"Hhh . . . he was a mmm . . . man," Wyck started.

"Was he a student at the school?" asked Wells.

"I object," said Thomas. "Counsel is leading his witness."

"He may do so to this extent," said the judge, "in the interest of time."

"Hhh . . . he was the eee . . . electrician," said Wyck.

"Let me understand, do you mean that Faye James got in the automobile with you?" asked Wells, aghast with shock, saying by his tone, these plotting, brazen women.

"Yyy . . . yes," said Wyck.

"You had never met her before?" asked Wells.

"Nnn . . . no," said Wyck.

"And now tell us how you met Mary James. You had

gone to take a message from Carl to Faye, is that correct?" asked Wells.

"Yes sir," said Wyck.

"And what happened?" asked Wells.

"As I was driving along in my car, Faye saw mm . . . me, and called me over," said Wyck.

"And then?" asked Wells.

"I www . . . was telling her about Carl, and then Mary walked up."

"You mean on the sidewalk?"

"Yes."

"Then they both got in the automobile?" asked Wells.

"Yes," said Wyck, "and they asked me to take them to a movie."

"You went to the James house three evenings later?" asked Wells.

Mary played it in her mind, that evening long ago, like a used record, its grooves etched much too deep, the needle caught too far inside the caverns, it slowed and dragged at a funereal pace, the song, the singers, her mom, the ring . . .

Then Wells, glancing swiftly at her, marched over to the chair in which she sat. He pointed at her face, then boomeranged his look across the courtroom and asked his client, "How did you happen to go there?"

"Bbb . . . by invitation."

"Oh?" said Wells. "What invitation?"

"A ppp . . . postcard. I received it in the mail."

Dramatically, Wells walked over to his courtroom desk, where Tully was sitting among notes and briefs. From under the table he pulled a large steel suitcase, then motioned to a man standing at the back of the room, who came forward with a small steel key. Wells pitched the suitcase up to the table in front of the jury, then opened it ceremoniously to reveal Mary's letters neatly tied in package twine—stacks and stacks of them.

Mary stood to curse, her curse a prayer, "Jesus damn."

Thomas took her arm, pulled her down. "Wait," he said.

"I can't wait. I actually wrote those things, but if he reads them you won't understand them like I meant."

"It will be all right," said Thomas.

"It's not all right. They're using me. They're so cheap and they're so dirty."

Stifled whispers. Her dad reached out and held her arm the way he used to do when she was a little girl about to cross a dangerous street.

Wells reached into the suitcase and picked out a postcard of two little girls in straw bonnets. He waved it at the jury. Written by Faye, but signed by Mary, it said, "Yoo-hoo, remember us two?"

Mary cringed in her chair and strangled screams as Wells accused her of plotting to capture this rich white boy. Her mother pulled out a thermos of ice water. She wet a cloth and held it to Mary's wrist, an ever-expanding lifeboat, her mom.

Wells continued: Claiming she started her successful seduction six weeks later, reading a letter, ". . . I want to be with you always and I feel terrible sad when I do not see you each evening. I have had some Boyfriends but I have not fallen for them like I have fallen for you. I never have let a fellow touch me like you do because you make me feel so loving dear. But how would it be if you had me all to yourself? What you would do with me, I can imagine."

All out of context, out of order, secret meanings and shared wishes, private jokes. Wells said she had schemed for Wyck's money, listen to what she wrote to him in San Francisco. "I dreamt you bought me a bright new Hispano Suiza and you filled the trunk with piles and piles of brand new hundred dollar bills."

"She threatened him into marriage," said Wells, pulling out a letter she had written in great frustration. " 'This is the last letter I will write. Your being rich came first. When you are twenty one you can still come and get me if I am still here. Do not call me anymore unless you call to marry me.' "

Then Wells put into the record evidence of her teasing Wyck, a photo of her in a slip, sent to him in Hawaii, inscribed, "You can put your head on my pillow any-time."

There was a flurry in the courtroom. Thomas rushed up to Leon Tully and grabbed him by the coatsleeves. As loudly as he could, he said, "You pocketed that photo."

"I wanted to see it closer," Tully said.

"It was on its way to your pocket," shouted Thomas. "You were stealing court's evidence, or else you were going to leak it to the press."

"Those people don't break on curves," whispered Mary.

"They're sick and crazy tricksters," said her mom.

"Poor Wyck. Poor Wyck," Mary's words slipped out involuntarily, seeing Wyck captive of these evil people, worse than a moon eclipsing light forever, a night that stops all birds from singing.

Tully put the photo back in the suitcase. There was no proof of Thomas's charge, and Tully ignored it.

"*She,*" yelled Wells, recapturing the court's attention, "tried inventing stories about other men, implying that only with the greatest of effort was she able to be true. This she wrote from the Adirondacks, where she went with the Hubbards to care for their children: 'There are lots and lots of fellas here. Berlin, the Broadway chap has took a place next door. He has four friends and they are all swell kids. Al Jolson was in the swimming pool today and he is some man with the ladies.' "

Wells interrupted the reading of her letters to call Al Jolson, then a rising actor, to the stand. Jolson was in a hurry, the judge had allowed him to take the stand at his convenience. He had to play a matinee, he said with humor, but he had come to clear his name. After all, he was an honorary sheriff in Keokuk, Iowa. And people were talking to him about making the first movie in which anyone had ever vocalized (using this occasion to plug *The Jazz Singer*). He did not remember ever seeing this Mrs. Hanover. But his wife had locked him out of the house because she thought he was a rake.

Wyck returned to the stand. The courtroom had just been aired, there was a chill in it now that put them all on edge.

"Was there any talk before the marriage about color?" asked Wells.

"Yyy . . . yes. In September 1922, Mary told her mother that a friend, Kitty Corcoran, had married a Nnn . . . Negro jazz musician. Mrs. James sss . . . said she would do anything she could to keep her girls from marrying Negroes. They were not Negroes she said, they were English. She said the fff . . . first time they had seen a Negro person was when they arrived in New York."

"Did you believe Mrs. James?" asked Wells.

"Yes," he said.

"Was there anything said about the Jameses being of Spanish ancestry?" asked Wells.

"Mary told me she had met a Hhh . . . Harvard man in the Adirondacks and he asked her, What are you? She answered, I am of Spanish extraction."

Wells read from one of Mary's letters. "I met a young man who does not believe my people is English born. He calls me a Spanish kid. I said I was very glad that he liked me but we could just be real good friends and if he ever was in New York he could look me up and I would like him to meet my friend Mr. Edward. He is a graduate from Harvard College. He says I was real refined not like the girls he meets nowadays." Wells put the letter down. "Did you understand that a person of Spanish origin was sometimes dark in color?"

"Yyy . . . yes, I did," he said.

"Did you love her?" asked Wells.

"Yes," said Wyck.

"Did you know the social position of her family?"

"Yes."

"Their financial condition?"

"Yes."

"And you loved her?"

"Yes."

"Could you have loved her if you had known she was a Negro?"

Wyck's mother had hated even Negro servants, she said they were unclean, had worms in their bowels, stole white souls, buried unwanted infants alive. His father said they never prayed, and when they did, their Christ was Antichrist, black Jesus was a hoax. . . .

"Could you have loved her if you had known she was a Negro?" Wells repeated.

"Nnn . . . no," said Wyck. "As to color, I draw the line."

Chapter 18

■ MARY AND HER FAMILY, followed by scores of reporters, children, flappers, gawkers, were trying to find a restaurant in White Plains that would serve her lunch. Klan members jostled her as she walked. Men with armbands stood at the restaurants blocking her way. "Nigger . . . Nigger . . . We don't serve niggers here. Niggers should eat with niggers."

One owner turned out the lights in his cafeteria, closing temporarily to avoid bad publicity.

Lee Thomas had had it and angrily went into a diner to buy box lunches. They went and sat on a lawn in the park.

"It would have worked, the marriage," Mary was murmuring, mostly to herself. "If only they'd given it time." In her mind there was no hope for love anymore, but just because it had perished, did that mean it had not existed? No, indeed, the further away from love she got, the surer that love seemed.

They drank lemonade and coffee in the park. She knew she couldn't open a flask with Mr. Thomas there, he was temperate by choice, not by law, preferring, he said, to put strong things inside his body—and water was stronger than booze, it could hold up a whale.

"I'm just so weak from all of this," said Mary. "I don't feel I belong in this world."

"You do belong in this world, and it's a fine one, but it needs a few changes," said Thomas, glancing at the ring of Klansmen stationed near the park. "In a changed world there would be room for you and Wyck."

"I can't change the world, Mr. Thomas, but I can change myself. Did you think he'd read all those letters out loud like that, in court?"

"No, I didn't Mary."

"Mr. Thomas, if I lose, I could go to prison. I've heard about women's prison in Albany—stone benches, holes in the ground for toilets, rust in the water and rat tracks on the bread and crazy women, whores, and two jail sections, one for whites and one for Negroes."

"Mary, they won't send you to prison, I promise. But what about the letters you have? Why won't you let me use them? Just the sight of his stationery would probably shut this case up and shame them off the stand."

She sighed. "All right, Mr. Thomas, I have letters that will blow their fancy manners and their high pretending to the far side of the moon."

▪

LEE RICHARDS THOMAS STOOD facing Wyck Hanover, wanting to wring his neck, shake the life out of him, but he knew the jury and the judge felt Wyck was the underdog, the victim, the hapless, luckless lover. And the mob of melting women in the crowd would like Lee Thomas better if, instead of being harsh on cross-examination, he was gentle with the boy, considerate and kind. In fact, that was the only way to overcome their pity. So his voice was quiet and soothing, he assumed a bedside manner as he asked, "You had a little apartment fixed up for Mary Hanover, your wife, didn't you?"

"Yes," said Wyck.

"You had furniture in there, didn't you?" continued Thomas.

"Yes," said Wyck, his voice shrouded, wrapped up, mummified.

"Did you give that to her, that furniture?"

"I . . . I did, yes."

"And later you told Mr. Tully to take it away from her?"

"I ddd . . . did not," said Wyck.

"Has Mr. Tully told you that he took your wife's furniture—it didn't amount to much—took it out of her—your—apartment and put it in storage where she couldn't touch it?"

"Yes."

"He told you that?"

"Aaa . . . afterward."

"So Mr. Tully took it upon himself to take your wife's furniture away from her?"

"Yyy . . . yes."

"Does he often do such things without your orders?"

"Mr. Tully is not on trial," Wells interrupted.

"Objection overruled," said the judge.

"He is sort of the general in this case, isn't he—doing things without your orders."

"This is a highly improper line," Wells protested.

"Your objection has been passed on," said the judge.

"Nnn . . . not always," answered Wyck.

"Do you know in whose office he is working?"

"Mmm . . . my father's."

"Now, about those letters, Mary's letters, where did you keep them?"

"In . . . in a trunk, in our apartment."

"Did you object to Mr. Tully's taking them out of your trunk?"

"I told him it was all right later, after I signed the complaint."

"Did you, yes or no, did you object, at the time he did it, to his removing your wife's private, confidential letters from your trunk without your consent or authority? Well, he stole them out of your trunk, didn't he? Be frank."

"It wasn't in my power to prevent it."

"It wasn't in your power to control your own lawsuit, is that your answer?"

A leap of hope for Mary as she sat listening. If Thomas could prove that Wyck did not want to bring this suit, that he was kidnapped and a victim, maybe they would throw it out of court. Then she and Wyck could live together again as man and wife. But the leap was like a doe running through the forest, jumping quickly over fallen timber, running against obstructions and with a sense of risk. It didn't excite her, not at all. She was beginning to hate all men, and thought of breaking cocks like twigs to make a mattress in the forest.

"Do you consider yourself a man?" asked Thomas.

"Yyy . . . yes," said Wyck, knowing this was not an idle question.

"And a man of honor?"

"I sss . . . suppose so."

"And as a man and a gentleman, you were nevertheless willing to break your promise to this girl that you would keep her letters safe and private?"

"I hhh . . . had to."

"You didn't ask your lawyer not to read them? You allowed the private, personal feelings of a woman—a woman you say you loved—to be paraded here in court, in front of strangers. Didn't you feel that a man of honor might hesitate, might ask his counsel, might even tell his counsel that this was not an honorable thing to do?"

"I was told it was for my own benefit. I had to permit them."

"You were *told,*" said Thomas with great emphasis, "for your own benefit that you *had* to allow the letters to be read in open court, were you?"

"Yyy . . . yes."

"And as long as this was for your own benefit, you were willing to forget your promise to your wife, were you?"

"Yyy . . . yes."

His preamble over, Thomas now handed Wyck a copy of a letter and walked more copies over to Judge Morgan and Mr. Wells. "I'd like you to read this through yourselves," he said. Thomas leaned back to watch the faces of the men as they read Wyck's letter. He thought there was something comic in this scene. The mythical god Voltan was right in teaching his sons to live without happiness. The pursuit of happiness had gotten this young man in over his head.

Wyck finished reading and bent his head.

"You are a free agent in this lawsuit?"

"As I am aaa . . . advised, I will follow orders."

"Then you are not free to do as you desire in your case?"

Wyck said, emphatically as his stuttering would permit, "I . . . I . . . aaa . . . am free, yes."

"Do you still want to proceed with this lawsuit?" asked Thomas.

Wells started shouting, blustering, "That, Your Honor, is a deliberate threat to the witness that unless he discontinues this action, that letter will be read into the record of this court and made public."

"That is the most improper accusation that I have ever heard from a lawyer in a court of law," Thomas said.

"I am preventing you from intimidating my client," said Wells.

"You are trying to bring about a mistrial in this action," said Thomas.

"I am not. I am not doing anything improper, this is for a good and legitimate purpose, Your Honor," said Wells.

"I object to the continuation of this statement on the part of Mr. Wells," said Thomas. "It is a blatant attempt to poison and to prejudice. A younger lawyer at the bar would never dare to make it."

The judge turned to Wells. "Have you said all that you desire?"

"No, not yet," said Wells, looking down at the letter. He was sickened, but now it was too late for that, too late to buy this letter, and surely there were more like it, too late to have them stolen, make them vanish somehow. "I have read the copy of this letter. I am overwhelmed by its contents. I am somewhat of a one-track-minded man. . . ."

"I do not know what you are leading up to," said the judge.

"I am answering the question: Does my client wish to continue with this trial? Our answer to this threat, Your Honor, is yes, he does. We defy this lawyer, we dare him to do his very worst. We will proceed right now to lay this filth, as Mr. Thomas would have us do, right now bare in front of everyone."

"I was not the one to start this filthy business of reading private letters aloud in court, but I hope I will be the one to end it," said Thomas.

"Mr. Thomas, may I say that since you are about to read this letter, I do not think it should be heard by women. I would not want to stay if I were a woman."

Morgan waited tensely, but only a few scattered ladies got up.

"Ladies, I am giving you the opportunity to leave now while there is a lull," said the judge.

Nobody rose.

Finally, exasperated, "I see you are not going to leave voluntarily. Under the law I have the right to clear the courtroom in any way I see fit. Anyone in the shape of a woman who has no business in this courtroom will leave now."

▪

IN THE YARD OUTSIDE the trial room, crowds of women, in varying moods, waited to be let back inside. A man came by selling copies of the letter, which he bragged would bring in money from as far away as Chicago. A woman handed him twenty-five dollars and started reading it to her friends. "My dear little dove. I bicycled through Griffith Park today and when I returned I found two more of your sunny notes. I feel so pleased dearest, when you write, and I love it when you tell me how you remember fondling me and making me feel as if I were in Paradise. Mary, do you recall when you were lying in bed and I used to make you flush all over with my ardent mouth . . ."

Giggles and swoons.

INSIDE THE COURTROOM, THE letter had been read and Wyck was still on the stand. The messengers, young boys who run teletypes for the press, had been replaced by uniformed guards. It was, almost, an all-male audience.

"You were not so innocent as far as being able to make love to a girl is concerned, were you?" Thomas said to Wyck.

"I was, yes."

"Well, then, how did you go about making love to Mary?" said Thomas.

"Www . . . we rode around in the automobile."

"Now, if everyone who rode around in an automobile made love, we would have a lot more of it, wouldn't we? What did you do? That is what I am after."

"I . . . I put my arm around her."

"So that was your first move in making love to Mary Hanover, the one whom they claim snared you, or tried to. What was your next move?"

"I . . . I believe I kissed her."

"Oh, you kissed her? And what induced you to kiss her?"

"Hhh . . . human instinct."

"You knew before you kissed her that something inside of you dictated it was going to please you?"

"Yes."

"Well, that same human instinct prompted you to do more, didn't it?"

"Yyy . . . yes."

"Now, I want you to tell this jury what you did on the first night you went to the Marie Antoinette. How did you overcome this girl's resistance to you?"

"I believe . . . I . . . I played with her."

"What do you mean? There is no room for modesty here. There has been no modesty about revealing your wife to the jury, has there?"

"No."

"You have exposed the innermost recesses of her life, haven't you?"

"Nnnn . . . no."

"Your lawyers have done so, with your acquiescence?"

"They have done it."

"What do you remember doing in the car on the way to the Marie Antoinette?"

"I . . . I remember hugging and kissing her."

"What else?"

"I . . . I believe I put my hand under her dress."

"And then you asked if you could stay at the Marie Antoinette with her, didn't you?"

"Yyyy . . . yes."

"When you first asked her, she refused, is that right?"

"Yyy . . . yes."

"But after you kissed her and put your hand up her

dress, she agreed. You were not so dumb, then, were you? You played on her passions. You were not so innocent as you have been painted to this jury, were you?"

▪

THE NEXT DAY'S EDITION of the *Daily News* carried a box on the front page headlined: "TWENTY YEARS' PENALTY PROVIDED FOR AN OFFENSE LIKE WYCK'S." It continued, "Conduct such as described in Edward Wyck Hanover's letters to his wife is a criminal offense in New York State. Section 690 of the Penal Code prohibits such conduct and bans it as an Unnatural Act. The penalty for violating the section is twenty years in prison."

The *Mirror* announced a love letter contest with a weekly prize of twenty-five dollars for the best letter it received. Try to beat Wyck's, they said, but they also cautioned, "The letters must be printable."

Mary was pacing up and down in the courtroom study. Thomas had just explained to her that the news stories were correct, there were laws in the state of New York, statutes called Crimes Against Nature, Unnatural Acts.

They had called it visiting each other's streams.

"If it's wrong, how wrong is it? Can he go to jail?"

"If he were discovered in the act, but now he only risks fines for sending smut through the federal mails." Thomas was thriving on the letters like a crocodile in a warm swamp.

"Crimes Against Nature," said Mary. "A person is half brain, half body. Where are the laws that protect their body's side?"

"The law takes a different view," said Thomas. "It's purpose is to control our bodies, to put a brake on the animal in us. We are dual in our nature, it admits, but it idealizes the brain and denigrates the body. The animal side is the murderer, the rapist, the sloth; the mental side is the nurse, the loyal father, the builder. These are judgments that go far back, to the Buddhists and the early Greeks, to Plato—this belief that certain acts are bestial, just not natural to human beings. Anything that does not lead to procreation—coitus interruptus, contraception, any form of sodomy or oral sex—is forbidden. Such acts have been outlawed in Western civilization since the Old Testament. These forms of sex were considered unclean. Why, the Jews wouldn't eat bacon, let alone each other."

Thomas was finding comfort in teaching and making jokes. It masked his wonder that everyone was not like himself, pop-eyed at the sight of genitals, even his own. His sex life with his wife was brief, played out, having the same intensity as chicken broth.

It must be shocking for Mary, though, to suddenly realize she had broken not only a law, but an age-old taboo. She seemed as surprised as Oedipus when he realized he was sleeping with his mom.

"We didn't know we were doing anything wrong," said Mary. "Love is acts. These were acts of love."

"There are those who would agree with you, who feel it should be legal for two adults to express themselves however they want to. But the state of New York says—pardon me, but I have to be explicit, this is no birds-and-bees conversation we're having—that it is only legal for two adults, over the age of twenty-one, and married, to do it with the man on top and the woman on her back."

"That's all that is legal in New York?" asked Mary.

"Yes," said Thomas.

It was indeed a world she didn't understand.

COURT WAS BACK IN session, and Wyck was still on the stand.

"Did you love this girl?" asked Thomas, like a dog with burrs in its tail.

"Yes," said Wyck.

"And you were trying to tempt her with those letters, weren't you?" asked Thomas.

"I www . . . was not, no."

"You had no intention of exciting her sexually when you wrote this letter?"

"No."

"If that is true, why did you write, 'Darling, am I tempting you? Do you remember when we were alone together?' You didn't think it might tempt this girl to write about 'that something acting the way it did' when she was nearby?"

"She asked me to. She asked me ttt . . . to make my letters interesting."

"What were you referring to when you said 'that something'?"

After a long pause, Wyck managed to say, "Mmmm . . . my organ."

"You were talking about having an erection?"

"Yyy . . . yes."

"And you didn't think that might tend to tempt her sexually?"

"I object to this screaming at the man," said Wells to the judge.

"And I might object to Mr. Wells's saying 'Grrr . . . grr' this morning, directed at my client."

"That is a different thing," said Wells. "It was another tone of voice and it was in the hall. You are sneering at this man."

"I withdraw the sneer," said Thomas. "May I proceed, Your Honor?"

"Very well," said Morgan.

Thomas asked the stenographer, "Will you repeat the question in your soft voice?"

"And you didn't think that might tend to tempt her sexually?" said the stenographer.

"No, I did not," said Wyck.

"When you wrote to this girl, 'Sweetheart, when I am in bed it does the same thing and aches for your dear self to lie on me and hold it in your tender palms and very softly help it make its way between your heavenly legs,' you didn't think it was tempting?"

"Nnn . . . no."

"Was it amusing to you? Did it give you pleasant sensations to write this stuff?"

"Mmm . . . my being true to Mary. I hhh . . . had no other outlet to relieve my passions except my letters, and in them I put my heart and soul."

"Did you mean the things you said in these letters?" asked Thomas.

"Yes."

"Did you do the things you said in these letters?"

"Yyy . . . yes."

Thomas read, "Recall, Old Trooper, when I used to lie between your legs and get passionate with my tongue. You loved that, didn't you, baby girl? Can you feel me when I write of the times I picked up your robe and went to the end of the sheets and got beneath you? Oh sweetheart, do you remember when I asked you, come Mary come? My darling, when my mouth had made you blissful you would say to me, Kid, I am in Paradise."

It tested a man's endurance. More than one jury member held papers over his lap to conceal a hard-on, trying to retain his moral outrage but picturing those unnatural practices and wishing to be Wyck Hanover, if only for those two weeks with beautiful Mary in the Marie Antoinette.

Chapter 19

■ IT WAS ELECTION DAY, court recessed like a fly-reel stopped midair. Mary was dressed, sitting over a second cup of coffee in the kitchen. It was early, she watched the clock, she could be lounging in silk pajamas at the Coral, leading the life of a lotus eater, if not for all this madness.

She peeked through the dark, dense drapes that gave the house a claustrophobic air. There were always people trying to look through the windows, harsh and piercing stares, prying curiosity, a wish to crack and press and jam themselves into her world.

She was going out and she was scared, and yet it was important.

Don't go out, don't go out, a voice within her said, the Klan is following you, early is dangerous, late is worse. She planned to go at eight o'clock through the back and ditch the Klan, stationed near the front.

They were grinning and unnerving, but they did not notice her as she slipped through the little woods behind the house, past the grocery store with its candy cases and refrigerated pop, and past the railroad station into Felham. She was lucky, she did not have to cross town to reach her destination. She came to the square, where the Hanover bell watched her like an iron eye. She waited for it to clang in ancestral outrage. It didn't. Ha, ha, she said to the bell, you can't ring now, you're silenced. Stilled. You're dead.

MARY WAS GOING TO vote. No woman in her family had ever voted. It had been three years since the women's suffrage law was passed, and all that time the idea of voting had grown in her like a bulb working its way out of the darkness, splitting the earth, struggling and tunneling to be in the open air.

During the war, lots of things made sense that hadn't made sense in peacetime. Like the idea of women working—taking men's jobs and driving trucks and dealing with money and actually acting like men while two million men went off to war. And since they were working, women assumed an importance in their own minds, like Mary, she was a patriot, a partner with men. So why, when the war was over, should she go back to being just another girl, having fun and thinking only about marriage?

She had always been told to follow rules, follow rules. A chant she'd heard forever. Make yourself useful, volunteer at the hospital, become a pen pal to an orphan, lead a group of Camp Fire Girls, or write a cookbook for the church. And especially don't do anything that would make you seem pushy or unmarriageable, or you might end up a spinster following the same old rules, even worse rules, and lonely, living for the day when a man might come along to marry you, and even though you were seventy and wrinkled and shriveled and used to life alone, any woman should accept any proposal of marriage with the joy of a sailor rescued from a desert island. Those were the rules and voting was against them.

It was time to break the rules.

Many women, not just Mary, had realized that they could vote—it needn't be a sordid thing, politics was not so complicated or removed from them. It had to do with education, children, and the price of food and clothes, and expanding the charities they worked for, protecting the old and the sick, things that touched their lives. It needn't mean wanting to be like men, but the world was being run by men and maybe they needed some help. Why, after all, couldn't America be a kind of co-venture, so the things that women wanted wouldn't have to be handed down or out?

She had begged her mother and her sisters to vote with her. Her mother said she only voted for the Lord. Her mother wouldn't drive a car. Sylvia had said she was too ignorant to vote. Footsie Fuller said he would boot Faye out of the house if she ever went near the polls and tried to run the world. They were still following the rules. They believed the antivoting literature, illustrating the Horrors of the Deserted Home, unwanted and unwashed children playing with safety pins and matches, teetering out of second-story windows, women in short hair, wearing trousers, smoking and drinking at bars. They said these suffragettes might be part of the Red Menace, pictures showed them in cell meetings with angry faces, pounding tables, Bolsheviks, man haters, women with no makeup and cotton stockings trying to undermine the government.

But Mary was not a radical. She was very feminine (though her chances of being a mother seemed to lessen every day, in fact her chances of staying married seemed nil, the Hanovers had won that victory), she was not an Unnatural Woman. That was what the pamphlets said about Angelina and Sarah Grimke, who were really Quaker converts from a prominent slave-holding family in South Carolina who published the first theory of women's rights in America. They said women finally sought the vote when they saw Negroes could get it, the suffrage movement crystallizing within the abolitionist movement. And it struck her now, even then, women had identified with slaves. Maybe race was not the issue, occupation was.

Wyck had always told her she was strong and independent and she did things for herself. But was that true? Now she saw that the idea of service was deep within her. Not only because her mother had been a servant was it honorable, but her father had always said that servitude was good and ethical, and success was best if it was a form of service. Gerald Barton's popular book, *The Man Nobody Knows,* which her father had just read, taught that Jesus was a great executive. "He picked up twelve men from the bottom ranks of business and forged them into an organization that conquered the world. His parables were the most powerful advertisements of all time. In fact, Jesus was the founder of modern business. Why, you ask? Because he was the author of ideal service." George had encouraged his daughters to go into service, they took jobs making beds and ironing and taking care of people's children.

She remembered when Wyck had given her stocks, twenty-four shares each of New Haven Clock, Emerson Shoe, and Chicago Standard at eight percent interest, the night they had gone to the mayor's to be married, saying, "Mary, I want to do well by you." She had fondled her stocks for a day or two and passed them on to her father. Just like that. Never a thought about keeping them, managing them herself. She was thinking about such things now. She would order "Common Sense with Money" and "A Guaranteed Income at Eight Per Cent" from the Investment Section of the paper. How would he react to that, to his daughter wanting to manage her own affairs?

And how would he react to her going to the polls? She hadn't asked.

She had seen him change since the story broke. He had been made defensive, pleading her case at the drop of a dime. Mary's heart broke for her father, coming home from the trial each night, chewing on the case as though the morality of the world rested on its outcome.

Her father was now declaring his race openly, wearing it like a badge on his coat or an armband on his sleeve. Mary, too, felt she should say it before every conversation. "Hey, there's something I want to tell you about me, before we go on talking, I mean it might make a difference to you, you wouldn't want to keep talking to me or take me out or have me to your house for dinner."

Her father still didn't know his birthplace or his birthday, he would justify it, telling truths of history, "Lots of people don't know when they were born, they tell it by the seasons, or before they built the bridge, or after the harvest, or around the time of a flash flood. Believe it or not, time used to pass unmarked, without birthday parties and hats and balloons and frosted cakes."

She stood on the street, crowds were watching her, and then she went into Dellby's Barber Shop, which had a big flag poking out in front, giving status to the shop, and importance as a poll.

Faces fell like bricks on glass, bodies twisted with disapproval like young trees in a storm. But she was used to disapproval now. One more angry stare was nothing. It no longer shook her, made her body quake, or gave her scary dreams. She was newly comfortable with the idea of being different, of doing what her heart, or fairness, asked. She traveled through unnatural quiet, pencils stopped, breaths held, looks exchanged. A corridor of men. "I want to vote," she said.

She was silken and she wore a simple dress, looking prim, but not prudish, like a drawing of a Vogue pattern. She slid up to the voting counter in challis and blue. Almost as soon as it began, it was over—a vote of confidence for Coolidge, who would keep us out of war; absentee ballots for soldiers and sailors in hospitals and rest homes; pay increases for police and firemen; home rule for cities, and special Christmas lights on Main Street; and votes for City Council members whom she'd known since birth.

That idea, the bulb, that had brought her to the poll, was now a flower. She shuddered then, to feel the way a slave might feel, tunneling out of the underground railroad and popping into a friendly kitchen in the North, grateful like annuals for sun. Mary in her lovely dress and shining hair. She could not pick cotton, she would break her nails; she could not eat grits and ham hocks, it would destroy her diet. But she could declare herself a voter. One Mary James, equal to one William Hanover. And if there were enough of her and more of her than them—the Mrs. Rices and the Mr. Wellses—then it could be a world with more fairness and more goodness and more looking at people for what they are and what they really do.

When she walked out of the barber shop she was feeling strong, but now on the street her strength was tinged with fear, growing like the stain of coffee on a sugar cube. Surely the Klan would know by now. Someone touched her arm and she jumped like a doe and froze, but it was Councilman Pryor with his wife and the librarian and the mayor, and they were gathering around her like a cloak. "We are glad you came to vote, and if you'll wait for us," said Mr. Pryor, a balding man who owned a radio store, "Mrs. Pryor and I would like to drive you home. You must be tired and there are lots of people in the street. The car is parked out back. We've bought a new sedan. Anyone can buy four doors now. They're not available only to millionaires."

Chapter 20

■ WELLS HOPPED UP TO the stand. He was an old man. It was a crooked hop like a sparrow on one leg. This case was probably his last, he was ready to retire, felt he must win, he could not go out with a loss and this was so prestigious, such notoriety in this case.

The crowds stood three deep in the courtroom every day, the National Guard was monitoring the scene, defiant letters were being sent to judge and jury, a brick had just the other day been aimed at William Hanover, Jr., from the windows of a New York high rise. Millions of words had been teletyped from White Plains to newspapers all over the world. There were editorials in every New York paper, headlines in France and Germany, the case now called by the press "The Most Passionate Love Life Ever Declared in Public Places."

The Negro press was crowing. Why, only yesterday, the *Amsterdam News* wrote, "There are those who believe this story is better left unprinted, but we believe any story which shows the white man's humiliation due to his foolish stand on race should not be kept from the public eye.

Let us not spare him, for he has never in our history, spared the likes of us."

No rose water here.

This was life or death. Wells was ready to nail any man, woman, or child, he didn't care who, to save his client. No, this was not a case to lose.

SOMEONE ONCE SAID THAT Hanovers thought in centuries ordinarily, in generations often, in years only under pressure of unusual circumstances, and in shorter periods never. Hanovers hired people to deal with temporal matters.

Yet here was William Hanover, Sr., bending over daily newspapers, plotting in his study night by night with Fowler, Clark, Cox and Hyde, drawing up briefs. His study, the air thick with cigar smoke and manly odors, was filled with law books, bindings cracked, their pages creased and automatically opening to fraud, annulment statutes. He had his own court reporter quietly hidden in the crowd, secretaries laboring all the long night to bring their work to Wells in the morning.

William paused often for comfort from timeless sources, digressing on biblical authority for racial division (Genesis 9:25, 26, 27; 12:5; 16:9; 24:35, 36; 27:12, 13; Exodus 20:17; Leviticus 19:19; 25:44, 45, 46; etc., etc., etc.). He searched out passages of natural history, favoring "The Prognathous Theory of Man," which taught that Negroes were, in fact, another species—"prognas, derived from pro (before) and gnathos (the jaw) indicating the muzzle or the mouth of the Negro is anterior to the brain; their spinal cords are larger, their brains a tenth smaller, and their nostrils open higher, thus the Negro approximates the simidae (for instance he can detect snakes by smell alone). All the senses of the Negro are more acute, but he is less discriminating than the European. He has a good ear for melody, but not for harmony; a keen taste for food but not for flavor; and a servile nature, being a creature of feeling and imitation with no capacity for reflective faculties."

Looking like a portrait statue of a German monarch, his jaw held rigid and sharp like the cutting edge of military tin, William alternately pontificated and judged the progress of the case. The judge was like an iceberg with no tip; Wells lacked firmness with him. Wells dealt with detail like the Old Masters, with too much confidence, letting small things slide. Thomas was winning far too many points, perhaps a better lawyer could lead the judge more, cut off Thomas's foolish cross-examinations.

Still, Wells had proven his worth that very morning by discovering new evidence that would chomp up this family, cut their ragged credibility to shreds. Compromise was so impossible, a negative verdict so accursed, vile, horrific, that they had to look for fast surprises, fight sharp, swift battles, never think of sparing feelings.

The boy, of course, would rot in Hell forever, thought William, who had already made plans to bury him outside the family plot, their lot kept pure of sinners, doubters, desecraters—the dead of centuries should rest in peace among their own, their tombstones boasting "God Shops for Heaven Here."

William should have kept the boy the way the medieval Jansenists kept their children, in a cage opened only once a week. This was done with parrots to teach them how to talk, no more expected here. This boy was so stupid they had overestimated his wit, and thus he had outwitted them for sure.

How could he have written those letters? Was perversity addictive? Would he find another filthy girl? Is that why William had avoided anything but neat and simple sex, dried, folded like clean laundry—if used, quickly cleaned and put back in place again? This girl must have taught his boy such sex—certainly no Hanover had ever done anything like this before, Hanovers were revolted by nasty smells, delicate about what was on their palate. He tried to imagine the two of them, doing the acts described in the letters, but his mind could not put a white man there. This was not a white man's act. This was an act of black and tan.

His mind dwelt on the picture of her in the papers. Physically, she looked like no one in the Hanover family. How had he been attracted to her? Hanovers were attracted to others of their class, in their line opposites did not attract. She was not beautiful as others claimed, the whole family seemed coarse and jarring. Jarring looks, even beautiful ones, were in bad taste, faces should fit in with their surroundings. What had possessed the boy?

Possessed. Yes, it must have been the Devil. That whole family was the personification of the Devil, the same Devil who had plagued him all his life. His large contribution to the Klan (given under an assumed name) was justified—the Klan would publicly chasten and make historical examples of these Antichrists.

His son. He shuddered at the word. His boy? How could he have played into the Devil's hand, spawned this viper?

And what would he do with the boy until the Devil came to claim him? Should he keep him locked up, put him in an institution, perhaps accuse him of incurable alcoholism? No, that would cause another public outcry. He would have to be "exported" once again. Oh, where were the Jansenists now that he needed them so badly?

He had had so much sadness in his life (this son Satan's idiot, another dead, his wife perished in a fire). He could not live and avoid winters, but he knew he could survive a life of winters only.

▪

PLEASE DO NOT HURT my mom, Mary whispered to herself as her mother took the stand. Her mom, so different from herself.

What was her mother thinking of her now, now that she had heard the sex parts of Wyck's letters read in court? Had her mother ever felt her body was a playground? Mary cringed and blushed and then remembered a reporter asking her mother on the courtroom steps, "Have your feelings changed about your daughter since the trial began?"

Mom had said, "My little girl," echoed from Mary's childhood with feelings soft and true, "my little girl is the sweetest girl in the world."

Guilt struck. Her mind as scattered as a stellar constellation, Mary felt she did not deserve that kind of love. She was out to change that now, bound to earn it, bound to become like a rubber roly-poly doll with sand weighing down its bottom so it always ended up on its base.

Mr. Wells had finished hopping. "You are the mother

of Mary James?" he asked Elizabeth James, now on the stand.

"Yes, I am," said Mrs. James.

"Speak as loudly as you can please."

"Yes, I am," said Mrs. James.

"It is awfully important that everyone, even those in the back, hear you, and I can hardly hear you myself," said Wells, but he went on with his question. "Now, madame, you have heard these letters read, have you not, the letters between Mr. Hanover and your daughter?"

"I heard all of what you read, but I couldn't tell you all of what is in them," she said.

"Mrs. James, please speak as loudly as you can. The jurors are straining to hear you," said Wells.

"She is very quiet-spoken." Thomas stood to help. He apologized to the jurors. "I know that this is hard for you."

"I'd like you to remember some dates," said Wells. "In December 1920, where was Mary working?"

"She did part-time work for Mrs. Hubbard," said Mrs. James.

"The evidence shows that Mary was away from your home from December 19 to December 23, inclusive, at the Hotel Marie Antoinette. Did you see Mary and Wyck enter the automobile and start out for the hotel?"

"I object," Thomas rose. "That question is full of duplicity. It is asked on the assumption that Mrs. James knew they were going to the hotel."

"I accept your criticism and withdraw the question. Did you, Mrs. James, see them when they started from the house?" said Wells.

"Yes," she said.

"Did you inquire where your daughter was going?"

"I knew they were going to the theater."

"And when did you next know your daughter's whereabouts?"

"The next day she telephoned to say she'd spent the night, and she told me not to worry about her."

"And did you inquire about her whereabouts at any time after that?"

"A few days later, I telephoned a friend to ask if she was there."

"What reply did you get?"

"She said Mary wasn't there."

"What further inquiries did you make as to your daughter's whereabouts?"

"I didn't make any."

"Did you notify the police that she was missing?"

"No sir."

"Or the Bureau of Missing Persons in New York City?"

"No sir."

"To your knowledge, did your husband?"

"No sir."

"The evidence also shows that your daughter was off at the Marie Antoinette again for two weeks in February," Wells continued. "Did you make any inquiries at that time?"

"I did not. I thought she was working, that is all."

"How far from you was the place where she worked?"

"A few miles."

"You didn't call to ask about her?"

"No sir."

"Did Mary give you any account of her absence when she returned?"

"No sir."

"And you didn't make any inquiries?"

"No."

"A man came to your house while Mary was away and asked if Wyck Hanover was there, didn't he?"

"Yes."

"And you didn't make any connection in your mind between Mary's whereabouts and Wyck's?"

"No sir."

"Now, Mrs. James, where were you born?"

"In Huttoft, England. H-u-t-t, it is a funny word to spell."

"I understand that you were working near Huttoft on the same estate as Mr. James when you first met him?"

"Yes sir."

"You knew he was a colored man."

"He was a mulatto. In England there is no stigma to that."

"In what capacity did you work there?"

"I was a cook and he was a coachman."

"What sort of estate was it?"

"A gentleman's estate, a gentleman's private estate."

"Who lived on the estate?"

"An elderly gentleman. He had had a daughter living with him, but she left when she got married."

"How long had you been working there before you married Mr. James?"

"About a year, near as I can remember."

"And how long after your marriage did you leave England?"

"Soon after that."

"In what year?"

"1891."

"On what ship?"

"The ship *America.*"

"I would like to put in evidence the log of that ship," said Wells, his voice like the sound of electricity hitting water. "According to the log from that year, you brought with you to the United States a white child named Susan."

Mrs. James's daughters looked puzzled, polling each other in the courtroom with quizzical looks. A child named Susan? They had never heard about this.

But Mrs. James had confided in Thomas, and he now leaped to his feet, making the most vigorous objection he had yet made in this bitter case. "Are you really going into this, Mr. Wells?" His face was red. His voice shook. His hand trembled. Thomas, as a youth, had worked in Wells's office, they were supposed to love each other, but here was a gust of burning hate.

"I am going into it," said Wells.

"Thirty-two years ago? Until this moment none of her children have heard about the existence of a sister called Susan. She was sent back to England twenty-eight years ago," said Thomas, now pleading to the judge.

"Not sent," Wells hissed. "She was sold for five dollars a month to a man in Norwich County. It seems to me there is a question here of whether this woman guarded, as you contend, her daughter, or instead acted as a madam, pushing her out for money."

"Mr. Thomas," said Morgan, "your objection is overruled. The witness must continue."

"Was George James the father of a child called Susan who came on the boat with you from England to America?" asked Wells.

"No, he was not," said Mrs. James.

Mary shielded her mother from the cameras, for the first time allowing photographs of herself to be taken. They walked down the courtroom steps, careful of the ice that lidded the puddles in the yard of stone, and she had images of snowmen, melting like the ice—Mother, Father, all the little snowmen slipping to the ground.

Who was the man, she wondered? Her mother's life in England was always a subject of silence for the family. Mary imagined it as best she could, the life of a servant from a family of servants, children put to work when they were able, no expectancy of adolescence.

"Over here," a photographer called, trying to get her full in the face.

"Mary, look around."

She remembered falling asleep in her mother's arms at night, trusting her so completely, protected, safe, inviolable. Trust so perfect she would never wake at night, her crib a fearless, tearless place, her pillows white, her toys kept mended, her pastel quilt a floating warmth around her back, its creases seemed like smiles.

But another child, a half sister, had been abandoned, perhaps while deep in similar trusting sleep. Should Mary mistrust her mother now? Was her father less than truthful, too? Was this trial fixed and rigged and hippodromed for her to lose her faith in those she loved? Was love a trampoline of glass?

Her mother's hand touched her hand, transmitting feelings of old trust like warmth from heated rooms. A leak could sink a boat, a blimp, but her mother's goodness was there for sure. Mother must have had her reasons. And there are some rocks you want to leave unturned.

The ride home was silent, nothing was spoken about the trial until dinner, when somewhere between the madrilène and the meat, Elizabeth James let go of that memory of a rich man years ago. She had been waylaid, trapped, assaulted at sixteen by an English actor at the height of his career, a dinner guest who came upon her in the pantry after too much cognac, smelling of the chicken she had cooked, and pulled her to him in the linen closet. She didn't scream, her terror, worse than pain, was overpowering, and it was over almost when it started, his heavy flesh a hammer banging through her thighs.

George James had just come in for dinner with the servants, and he saw her leave the pantry, tear-streaked, her uniform was ripped and soiled and she was trembling. He heard the actor go back into the dining room.

The next day he asked her if she liked it at the house.

"I have a mind to leave."

Having loved her from afar, he sensed that what he'd seen was something bad. Having loved her from afar, he dared now to get close. "Would you think of marrying me? You have a way about you, soft and quiet, like the very center of the earth."

He was a handsome man, steady, physical, and reverent. Here was a miracle.

George sat now, his fork in his left hand, in English manner precisely cutting all his meat before he took one bite. "I would have liked for that child to become a Madame Curie—born to the world for a reason I could see. It would have made the whole thing understandable. But"—he sighed—"she became only another housemaid."

"We couldn't keep her, Mary," said Elizabeth James. "We had just come to New York, and we had to take jobs living in with other families. The child was jaundiced, she was weak and ill. We just couldn't keep her."

Mary nodded, as if a nod could serve as absolution.

"The whole thing was over, it was done with, and I never told you," said her mother. "I didn't think I'd ever have to. But I should have, because it's hurt you now. You should have known that I, too, had an experience with a rich man, but I thought they were beyond comparing. You seemed so safe with Wyck. I didn't want to look at you and see my own fears reflected. I wanted you to be a portrait of your own."

Chapter 21

■ HARLEM ON SATURDAY NIGHT was a playground, America's answer to Paris. Lenox Avenue cabarets were filled every night with handsomely dressed white slummers who danced the Charleston, heard the Jazz Age at its noisiest, and watched risqué reviews featuring high yallers, tantalizing tans, and hot chocolates.

The crowded Cotton Club catered only to whites. A black man was refused entrance just as an all-white stag party weaved up to the door. Wyck was among them.

His brother-in-law, Julien St. Paul Cosay, was celebrating his birthday with bootleg champagne. He had asked Wyck to join him, secretly breaking William Hanover's order that the family not see or talk to him. Julien's wife, Peregrine, had fled to Switzerland for the duration of the trial, refusing to write lest the press intercept any more letters. Their marriage always had been pomp, sex was no longer even circumstance. Julien's father had always kept a mistress, but Julien took after his grandfather—he preferred whores—making a sexual wake through New York exotics, Texas cowgirls, Asians, Indians, Hawaiians—anything out of the ordinary eroticized him (he had heard in kindergarten that Pocahontas turned cartwheels naked at social gatherings).

Wyck sat at the table like a man on a leash, watched by his ever-present bodyguard, Buddy Baker, a society detective quick at tailing wayward children, taking snapshots of adulterous mates, and restraining drunks in sanitoriums. Buddy was a betting man—he and Wyck would bet on anything, their major point of contact these days the World Series, which had just begun, the barber shop odds being the same for the Giants, 11 to 1 over the Yankees, as they were for Wyck, 11 to 1 over Mary. Their voices often rose in conflict over batting averages, homer records, Baker glued to WEAF Sports, and Wyck, a fifty riding on the pennant, felt a growing lack of interest in his case hitting home. Let his lawyers care. Let his father care. He was better at spectator sports, he did not choose to be a player.

He had decided to agree they were right (Father and Aunty and Peregrine and Tully), but in making them right, he had made Mary wrong, and himself wrong, too. She was a toy / he was a child; she was a slut / he was a virgin; she was uneducated / he was a fool; she was a liar / he was gullible. That is what they said, and he couldn't believe just half the story.

A beautiful young Negro girl came up to the table and handed him a card. "I am a slumming hostess for Inquisitive Nordics. Here in the world's greatest city it would both amuse and interest you to see the real inside of the New Negro Race. There are very few who know. I am in a position to carry you through Harlem as you would go slumming through Chinatown."

"No, thank you, dear," said Julien, tweaking her on the

behind. "Your nipples, dear, are hard as little black seeds, and your twat must be juicy and wet as a summer watermelon. I'll see the inside of the Negro race a little later."

He turned to Wyck. "See, you can talk to them. You can lay them and pay them. You just can't marry a coon, that's all."

"It . . . it was an error," said Wyck. "A mistake. It must have been black magic."

MARY WAS GOING TO make a speech. Lee Richards Thomas had told her there was to be a special community meeting in Harlem, would she please talk, say anything she liked, it was a way to share her problems.

"Anything I like? Can I talk fashions?"

"Anything you like," said Thomas.

"These people won't know fashions. They're all brains. I don't have that kind of a roof-God to run the show. My legs are in it along with my mind."

"You'll like these people," said Thomas. "Darrow and I think they're interesting."

"Is Darrow colored?"

"No."

"Will he be there?"

"No."

"Does he socialize with them? Do you? Will I?"

She had never been in a black ghetto before. She walked with Thomas through Harlem, past the ads for hair pomades and skin bleach, past the junkies and the hookers and the numbers runners. It unnerved her. "I could have been a model, don't you think?" she said nervously. "Walk around like I own Saks. Or live in Paris and go bare-legged and dress in gauze and smear so much kohl under my eyes they look like ripened plums. I could be just like Kiki, she's American and she's in *Vogue.* I don't speak French, but you don't have to. Someone in Paris, Miss Maud Loti, is getting famous for saying 'shit' in public. I like poetry and I could learn to mold Jell-O to look like fish and carve figures out of ice so when people came to the gallery to see my work it would be melted."

"Yes, Mary," said Thomas. "You could still do that."

"I'd feel more at home in Paris than here," said Mary, looking around her. "But I'm all done with adventure."

"Deferred is not abandoned," Thomas said.

"Shit," said Mary. "See, I'm practicing my French."

Mary had a tough case of lonelies. She felt abandoned, not deferred. It had been more than six months since Wyck left, and she was afraid she could never outlive his history, there was no place, no country where she would not have unasked-for visions of their passion. Now at night she healed herself, trying to throw off that energy she didn't want between her legs, which grew until her hands became helpless as the ocean pulled in and out by the moon. (Mrs. Hall said the only danger in masturbation was that it was bad for anyone to perform an act of which he or she disapproved, but that masturbation provides pleasure and also relieves emotional tension.) Waves are a richer blue far out at sea, stars brighten away from city lights—nature saves some great intensities for private. It was a wondrous thing, a form of holding. She wrapped her arms around herself, climbed nipple mountains, her tongue like custard, and made her own heart move.

▪

A FEW BLOCKS AWAY from the Cotton Club where Julien was pinching the butt of a Negro girl in tights (sanitation laws made colored girls, unlike white girls, cover up their legs), Mary, surrounded by the black literati of the day, stood up to make her speech. Writers, poets, artists, and sculptors, a black world alive with such people as Jesse Faucett, Countee Cullen, W.E.B. Dubois (who had just commented in *The Crisis,* "If anything more humiliating to the prestige of white America than the Hanover case has occurred recently, it has escaped our attention."), Langston Hughes, all members of the "New Negro Renaissance," "The Ebony Flute," were in attendance.

Thomas escorted her to the podium. He had worked with Mary on improving her English. (And she had been to Madame Louise to learn correct social procedure— "Memorize what I tell you, forget your instincts. Babies do things by instinct and they urinate in their pants." Mary had left. She knew the rich had no fun, and now she wondered if they had no brains.)

"I feel out of place with you writers and thinkers. My Daddy says I'm a dumbbell flapper with gumballs for brains," said Mary, warming to their friendly laugh. "I may be dumb but I want to be honest. I am not a Negro. I feel like I'm white. It takes courage to say that because people think I'm hiding, or trying to pass. But I've been brought up as a white girl. And I can't get all hyped up about this Negro pride and Negro heritage stuff. Maybe you can, and I'm jealous of you. It's yours. You feel you are Negro and you are proud of it. You must have found a way to live with the bad stuff.

"In Felham, in 1920, being white was better than being black, and I was arrogant about it. I wouldn't be seen on the black side of town or with a Negro, and now suddenly, I'm being asked by a lot of people to move my family and my residence over there. There've been bomb threats. And my dad's got a police dog.

"Another strange thing that's happened: I used to take children to school and work in the laundry of the New York Athletic Club. People now say I worked as a maid. They never called it that before. But now they seem to think I should dress up in a stiff black uniform with a ruffly white apron and teach white girls how to dance.

"The issue of sex, I am told, is a giveaway as to my Negroid race. I liked it. Yes, it was hot. I sure took to sex. And if enjoying sex makes me Negro, then for sure I am Negro. So I guess I should be a maid and change my neighborhood.

"Let me tell you some more things I have been asked to do because my race is now perceived as being different from what it was:

"One. Endorse a dancing school for the teaching of the Charleston (I was surprised they didn't mention the Black Bottom, it must have been a diplomatic group of entrepreneurs).

"Two. Take a job as a buyer of lingerie in a famous store in Harlem owned by white money. They even suggested I could start up a line of lingerie with my name on it.

"Oh, I'm so tired of noise and people and the putting on of hats and hose and polished shoes that shine and don't reflect a thing. And they want me to put on underwear and dance.

"Three. I've been asked to go on a lecture tour to speak about 'The Exploitation of the Black Woman in a Capitalistic Society.'

"And one more thing, number four. Harry Six, my banjo teacher, has let it out that I can sing. So I have an offer from a night club to sing and also to play, and I am quoting from the letter, 'the instrument that has so often brought solace to the people of your race.'

"It'd be silly if it weren't so sad," and the tears started to roll down Mary's flushed and fragile face. "Well, I'm not moving and I'm not getting up a banjo act. And I can't be an inspirational heroine of Modern Negro History. Because I'm just plain old Mary with the starch gone out, famous because one big galoot went and took a whole lot of love away from her."

Chapter 22

■ WELLS HAVING RESTED HIS case, it was now Thomas's turn. He surveyed the courtroom. He would be calling only faces known to all, no surprise witnesses, his job to show the prejudice, coercion, lying, and concealing that was taking place. He would defend her from their case and try to destroy the impression created by Wells that the Hanover side was entirely honest and reliable. He would not argue details, burden the record with more words, he knew that would be like going to smell flowers but inhaling bees.

He watched Mrs. James comforting the sad, very lonely Mary, looking wasted and wan. He suspected that his sympathy for Mary was more than just professional (in an unchanged world, was there room for such a feeling?). He hoped very much that he could help her, he would try now to plant some seeds that would sprout mammoth vines like Jack's, and let a giant down.

His first witness was Raymond Stark, called back to the stand. Thomas asked him about the visit he and Tully had made to the James house on the eighteenth of May.

"Didn't you go to Felham in order to persuade Wyck Hanover to leave his wife?" Thomas asked.

"I did not," said Stark.

"You and Mr. Tully had not discussed the possibility of having to hurt this girl?"

"Certainly not."

"Did you hear Mr. Tully say to this girl and her parents, 'You want to look out, you want to be careful. There is a lot of excitement about this. The Ku Klux Klan may burn down your house'?"

"I heard no such statement."

"You didn't hear it?"

"No."

"Will you swear it was not said?"

"I will not swear it was not said, but I will say I did not hear it."

"Did you do anything in particular when you were there?"

"We just had some conversation and talks."

"Nothing else? Take your time. No hurry."

"At the moment I don't recall anything else."

"Please think back, are you sure you did nothing but talk?"

"I may have taken Mr. Hanover's signature on a few papers."

"Did you just think of that?"

"Yes, I did."

"On how many papers?"

"I don't know. Five or ten or maybe twelve."

"And this just occurred to you?"

"Yes."

"What were the papers?"

"I believe they were some mortgage papers, bonds come due."

"Could they have been sixty thousand dollars' worth of mortgages signed over to Tully to get this law suit started?"

"I don't recall just what they were."

"When Mr. Hanover signed these papers, they were folded up, weren't they, so that just the line for signature was visible?"

"No, I don't think they were."

"Why do you hesitate?"

"Because I'm trying to think."

"Can't you remember?"

"Not exactly."

"When did you next do work for William Hanover?"

"I object to that question," said Mr. Wells.

"Excuse me," Thomas said. "When did you next do work for Mr. Tully?"

"I took Edward Wyck Hanover's signature on the annulment papers, the complaint."

"Where were you when he signed his name?"

"At the Ninth Street Station of the Hudson Tubes."

"Isn't it strange to sign a complaint in the subway?"

"It was near my office and he just came down to sign it."

"And then you signed it yourself, as the notary."

"To the best of my recollection."

"Why do you quibble about recollection? It would be the most natural thing in the world for you to notarize it with the same pen."

"Yes."

"Isn't it customary for a notary, when a man swears, to

put on his acknowledgment immediately?"

"If it is convenient."

"It was just as convenient for you to sign your name as it was for Edward to lean the papers up against a board in the subway station and sign them?"

"Yes."

"In view of your testimony, please look at this paper and explain the difference in pen points. They are not signed by the same pen, are they?"

"I don't believe I had my seal with me at the time."

"You knew you were going to take his verification but you left your seal behind?"

"I left it at my office."

"Now about the complaint itself, it was complete before you verified it?"

"I don't remember, I think it was."

"As a notary, you wouldn't take a signature on an incomplete document, would you?"

"No."

"Of course not. So the complaint was complete?"

"Yes."

Thomas hacked away, numbed and pressed Stark, skirting words that would give Wells cause for interruption or objection, putting corks on doubts to surface them like facts.

Mary watched. Thomas occasionally nodded to her, they spoke in signs, his lashes like the fingers of the deaf, signaling to her his expertise, his calm, his craft in threading souls through the needle of the law.

▪

THOMAS NEXT CALLED LEON Tully to the stand, his dislike for the man clearly evident as he snapped his questions to him. "How long have you been practicing law?" he asked.

"Since January 1906," said Tully.

"And whose offices are you in?"

"My own offices."

"With whom are you associated?"

"I am not associated with anyone."

"Well, who else is in the office with you?"

"The estate of Mathilda Hanover, the estate of William Hanover, Charles C. Cox, Newbold Hyde, C. J. Oakley Hanover, William Hanover, Jr., and Harry Puccino. Those are the names on the door. In addition, there are the Edman Wilkes Realty Company, the Pacific Mortgage Corporation, the Hawaii Realty Company, and the estate of Cornelius B. Wyck. I think that is all," said Tully.

"These companies you mention, are they companies that belong to the Hanovers?" asked Thomas.

"The Hanovers hold stock in these companies."

"Let's turn to the complaint itself. Did you draw the original bill of particulars in this case?"

"Mr. Wells drew it."

"From whom did he secure the information for it?"

"From me."

"From whom did you secure it?"

"The plaintiff."

"And did the plaintiff in this action tell you that the defendant represented to and told him she was white and had no colored blood, and that at the time the defendant made such representations, she knew them to be false and untrue?"

"I object to that. Mr. Thomas is calling for a communication between an attorney and his client," said Wells.

"Overruled. You may ask the witness if he got the

information from his client," said the judge.

"I did," said Tully.

"Is there anything in the complaint that you did not get from the plaintiff?" asked Thomas.

"I cannot answer that question in any way," said Tully.

"But you can say that the report you gave him was what Wells used in writing the complaint."

"Yes."

"And you gave him a correct report."

"I certainly did."

"After Wells dictated the report, you took it back to your office and put it in the form it's now in?"

"I took the paper on which I had taken his dictation, and gave it to my stenographer, who typed it."

"Have you Wells's original dictation?"

"I don't know. If I may be permitted to look in my folder, I might have it." Tully walked to the table and started looking through his things.

"Don't misunderstand me, sir," Thomas said to Wells. "I am not asking this to make any reflection on you."

"Oh no," said Wells.

Tully gave up searching and said, "I don't find it. I don't think my stenographer gave it back to me."

"Well, when you finally put it in its present form, did your client read it over and sign it?"

"He did, or at least I presume he did."

"You don't remember if he read it?"

"I was not present at the execution of it. Mr. Stark took the signature."

"So you don't know if the plaintiff ever agreed with the complaint you drew up for him."

THOMAS THEN CALLED WYCK. The trial had now lasted three whole weeks. Wyck's major chore was reduced to keeping his body quiet—his guts from grumbling, hands from shaking, gas from passing, howls from coming. He answered questions without thought to their consequence, it was simply not his problem, not his problem anymore.

"Mr. Hanover," said Thomas, "because of your affliction of speech I want to be gentle as I possibly can with you. Do you understand that?"

"Yes."

"And will you keep carefully in mind that if I ask you any questions which you do not understand, you are at liberty to say so?"

"Yyy . . . yes."

"I will try to make my questions clear to you. Now, your mind is all right, isn't it?"

"I believe it is."

"Your trouble is that you stammer."

"It is."

"And as you sit here, Mr. Hanover"—he was very sympathetic—"you don't want Mr. Wells or this jury or anyone else to gather the impression that you are an imbecile, do you?"

"Nnn . . . no."

"You don't want this jury to believe that you are not mentally sound?"

"No."

"Mr. Hanover, you left your wife this April of 1923, is that right?"

"Yes."

"And did someone accompany you when you left her house?"

"My attorney, Mr. Tully."

"Mr. Tully hurried you into the automobile, didn't he?"

"I went of my own initiative."

"Did I ask you that question, Mr. Hanover?"

"Yyy . . . you asked who hurried me."

"I will repeat my question. He hurried you into the automobile, did he not?"

"Nnn . . . no."

"What? The answer is yes, isn't it?"

"I hurried into the automobile."

"You hurried?"

"Yes."

"So you are able to make that distinction, aren't you? Your mind is working very clearly now, isn't it?"

"Yyy . . . yes."

"All right, where did you hurry to after you got into the automobile?"

"I went to Belrose, Long Island."

"Did you make any stops between the time when you left your wife and when you got to this house in New Jersey?" Thomas deliberately misquoted him.

Wyck said quickly, "It wasn't New Jersey. It was Long Island."

Thomas, glancing toward the jury to indicate that here was a witness who certainly had a very keen mind, said, "Oh yes, I'm wrong, you are right. You corrected me, didn't you?"

Mary watched Thomas plead, sneer, be ostentatiously polite. Wyck was blushing, stammering, sipping water, looking nervously around him. Mary felt like screaming Third Degree. How would she survive her turn up there?

Questions so confusing her that she, like Wyck, would end up feeding off herself, tasting her own limbs and blood, as Wyck was doing while he proved his mind was strong for Thomas.

Mary had once seen an idiot, standing on a street corner, nodding his head from side to side, twitching his eyes, curling his mouth, flicking his torso back and forth. He had been heavy with fat, not a muscle on his body, and his hair was full of grease and dust.

Wyck was not an imbecile. Wyck was as smart as most boys in her hometown. He could run a gas station, manage apartments, but he looked dumb next to these men, next to geniuses like his father or his brother or these lawyers. Harvard smarts, brain giants, they were fish who change the whole size of the sea.

Like a Bromo in a glass of water, she felt herself dissolving, people seemed like boats, drifting back and forth, near and far. Wells the knife edge of a sail. The judge a tanker, Thomas a canoe tipping in and out of reeds. And Wyck, an elegant ship of glass, water visible through its hull, turrets tall and slim, obscured by clouds, a sudden gust of wind could break it.

"When did you first believe your wife was colored?" Thomas asked Wyck.

"Whhh . . . when you announced it here in ccc . . . court." He spoke as though a large fish were caught in his throat, jerking and lurching for freedom. He signaled for another glass of water.

"But you signed a complaint asking for an annulment six months ago?" said Thomas.

"Yes," said Wyck.

"Did you read the document?"

"Yyy . . . yes."

"And you agreed to sign?"

"Yes."

"No one was holding a gun over you, were they?"

"I object to that," said Wells.

"Well, you are sort of being marshaled around here, aren't you, Mr. Hanover?" asked Thomas.

"Are you making an issue of these guards, even here with half the crowd jeering at the boy? He is attended by two men, is that a crime?" asked Wells.

"What time did you go to that subway station to sign the complaint?" asked Thomas.

"Lll . . . late at night."

"How late?"

"Ccc . . . close to midnight."

"This is immaterial," said Wells.

"I am setting the scene, Your Honor," said Thomas. "So, by the time you arrived at this subway station you had convinced yourself that your wife was colored?"

"Yyy . . . yes."

"But you were never certain that she had colored blood in her veins until three weeks ago?"

"Yes."

"And you swore to this original complaint in April, didn't you?"

"I did."

"Do you remember swearing to this paragraph, 'That the consent of said plaintiff to said marriage was obtained by fraud. That prior to said marriage the defendant represented to and told the plaintiff that she was white and not colored and had no colored blood which representation the plaintiff believed and was induced thereby and entered into said marriage.' Did you swear to that?"

"It . . . it . . . was true."

"Which is true—that you did not know or were not satisfied that she had colored blood until this trial, or that you knew she had colored blood and that was why you left her?"

"I read her birth certificate. . . ."

"Won't you answer my question? You know both can't be true, don't you? In plain English, in April, you swore that she was lying to you."

"Yyy . . . yes."

"Now, which is true—that you knew she had colored blood in April or that you had doubts until this trial?"

"I . . . I had doubts until this trial."

"So you swore to something that was untrue in your original complaint?"

"No, because there was enough doubt in my mind . . ."

"There was enough doubt in your mind that you could swear emphatically that she was a liar?"

"From the newspapers . . ."

"Did anyone ask you about newspapers?"

"No."

"Well, then, answer the question."

"Whhh . . . when the story hit the papers I started to have my doubts."

"But you continued to sleep with her, didn't you?"

"I doubted her, but I . . . st . . . still believed her."

"Come now, you either believed her or you doubted her," said Thomas.

"Doubt and belief can exist at the same time," said Wells.

"But he slept with her even when he claims he doubted

her. How long had he been doubting? Can an annulment reasonably be pressed by a young man who needs two lawyers, two detectives, and a mass of legal documents to pass into a state of true belief?"

Judge Morgan interrupted. "Mr. Thomas, you are summing up your case before you have presented it."

Thomas turned on Wyck with energy enough to shrink the sea. "You got a good look at your wife's color, didn't you?"

"Yyy . . . yes," said Wyck, accompanied by snickers from the audience.

"You didn't think she was tanned by the sea or the air, this wasn't the season, was it?"

"Nnn . . . no," said Wyck.

"Is your wife the same color now as she was then?" asked Thomas.

"She lll . . . looks a little darker now," said Wyck, glancing at Mary, who looked just like a flying bird caught inside the courtroom—its body thwack, thwack, thwack, thrown against the windows, trying to get out, wings flapping, bones cracking and body breaking as it tried and tried, its fear a sound to burst your heart.

Thomas turned to the judge and said, "I would like to request that Mary Hanover be brought up to the stand. I want to ask Edward Wyck Hanover to look at the color of his wife's body."

Wells became rigid with shock. "You propose to exhibit the naked body of this girl in court? I strenuously object to any such performance whatsoever." He was choking and he had learned to choke in an audible way.

Thomas waited for the judge to make his ruling.

After a pause, Morgan said, "I believe Mr. Thomas

should be allowed to do this because of the importance to the court of whether the plaintiff ought to have known that his wife was of colored blood or whether he was justified in not believing so when he saw her body. We don't know what color her body is. She is covered up."

"I object to this as utterly incompetent, immaterial, and calculated unduly to influence the jury," said Wells.

"Overruled," said Morgan. And then, "This will be embarrassing for the young lady. I suggest that the jury, the stenographer, Mr. Wells, Mr. Thomas, and myself go into my chambers."

"And the plaintiff, he will have to identify her," said Thomas.

"You are actually intending to go through this farce of exposing her body and asking him if this is the girl whom he married? This is an indecent proceeding, Your Honor," Wells stammered.

Morgan stood firm. "There is no evidence of how she may have looked to the eye of the plaintiff, and for that limited purpose, it may be received."

▪

Mary had whispered to Thomas late last week, the attack on her mother so damaging and her fear that she would lose the trial so intense, "Do you know my body is darker than my face?" (Why such shame in saying this?) And Thomas, knowing she trusted him, was quick to answer his every question and obey his every command, asked her help.

He wanted to use Mary's body as evidence. To have her appear naked to the jury was an act so dramatic and ingenuous it would appeal and it would shock, and within this appealing, shocking content they might see her as Wyck Hanover had seen her—a woman of such breathtaking beauty, so desirable, so physically magnetic that nothing short of force could have kept him from her. Her social pedigree, her racial origins, even knowing that her father had been a taxi driver with Negro drivers—it just had not mattered to him. He would never have left her had he not been tricked and ripped from her by these henchmen hired by his father. He could not have borne leaving this creature, as each man on the jury might not have had he been given an invitation to stay (as he himself might not have, had he been gifted of that gorgeous, blooming sexuality).

▪

MARY, WEARING A WELL-FITTING tan dress adorned with a gardenia, went into the lavatory with her mother, emerging after a short time into the judge's chambers. She was now wearing a loose silken robe, tied at the waist. Trembling, rippling with modesty, weighted down by unshed tears, she was close to collapsing.

At Lee Richards Thomas's direction, she untied her sash and the robe fell open. Her skin, the look of marquisette, tissue, a beauty magnified by nature like a drop of water on a rose. Yes, with makeup and with powder, her face was lighter than her body, and as she dropped her robe it was as when a flower, in giving up its petaled layers, gives up a hold on life.

"How could you not have known?" asked Thomas.

Known, Wyck wondered? When he saw her body, should he have known the future, coldly questioned, Are you more than meets my blinded, awe-struck eyes?

Should he have known that fire was hot before he touched it as a child, or ice that covered winter ponds would crack upon his weight before he plunged into the chilly water, his father screaming, "How could he not have known?"

▪

The stage was set for Mary James Hanover to take the stand, wanting only the soft music of a prelude, the rising of the curtain, and a short prologue by her attorney. She sat in her chair, oblivious to the crowded audience, the anxious press, the judge and jury. Like a prima ballerina in a darkened room, she rehearsed her performance with closed lids, running through it step by step, her eyes were a distraction, she had to move with sureness coming from within.

Lee Richards Thomas took the floor. "I am determined," he said, in a voice so soft that ears were stretched to hear, "that this girl has had enough. I rest the case."

The court was stunned. Mary fainted, her pain like whirlpools, her very life endangered. She was at the bottom of a well.

Chapter 23

In his room at the Gramaton Hotel, Wyck lay in bed, the silence loud as any jazz band. Night was the closing of a door—shut in, shut out, he lay awake and thought about the trial.

The recent memory of her body wouldn't leave him, brought thistles to his hands and dryness to his throat and aches to every limb. It moistened his eyes with tears that would not dry, and made his heart not beat but come in spasms, like the movements of a newly captured animal, too loud, too large, too anguished for its cage.

He remembered Thomas asking, "Did you read the document?" He had said yes, but had he read it? He couldn't remember, he had gotten so confused, and when he answered yes to Thomas it was out of pride, and fear of Tully and his father.

He had testified that she had told him she was white, but had she really? He couldn't remember, he thought she once had made a joke about being a Spanish kid. A joke that now was like a splinter, a tiny flick of wood, but when it traveled to the bloodstream it was fatal.

This trial was like a guessing game, a quiz. Grade me, score me, tell me I'm correct—his life at home had always been that way. But with Mary, he acted from his heart and it had been right, she approved of what he did, liked as well as loved him.

Part of him felt like standing up in court and saying, I don't know, I thought I knew but now I don't. I'm so confused, please let me be. His mind was like a paper kite he once had held which flew so high he couldn't see it, and there was just a string left in his hand, a gentle tugging, that was all.

▪

MARY WATCHED HER MOTHER'S garden through the window. She had taken to timing the life of roses. Two, three weeks, they stayed so beautiful and then they dried and darkened, drooped and died. Their married happiness had just outlived the rose.

It was Saturday night, all was quiet, Mom and Dad were in the kitchen listening to the new radio Mr. Thomas had brought them as a present. The telephone rang. She answered the ring and heard his voice, his voice like fragrance, her lily groom.

He begged, "Please come to me, Mary, please come just once. I'm so alone, I'm so sorry, Mary, please come."

He said if she had testified, he would have understood it better. She would have talked, he would have answered, argued, explained, protested, if only in his head. Now he would never understand at all. He had lost his bearings, it was true, lost his strength, like a swimmer trying to push off in the middle of a pool.

He needs me, he needs me so, she thought. He was so

pathetic, like a baby, he was teething, teething on her heart.

"Please, oh please, whatever it is that humbles a man is humbling me, Mary. My eyes are worse (would myopia go to blindness?), and I am depressed (would depression slip into insanity?). Please, oh please come."

Mary had promised that she would never cry in front of Wyck again. But tears kept inside may come out as perspiration. She would wear dress shields, and lie to her family, afraid that they would be afraid and tell Lee Richards Thomas, to whom everybody owed honesty at least.

Was pity as strong as lust and where would pity lead her?

"I'll come," she said, "but nowhere near a bed."

▪

THEY MET AT THE band shell in the public park at six in the morning, when the sun came up like slanted light hitting a wave. The dawn was sand surrounding broken things upon the beach, the shell itself abandoned in this private wood, thrown too far up from shore.

Pain heightens the awareness of nature. The air was full of tsk, tsk, the inward clicking of the wren. Light quivered around the trees like tongues, and animals were there. She hid her fur collar from a fox who was glaring at her from a parry pinyon tree. Rabbits twitched and bristled at the interruption of their morning meals.

The park itself, deserted, seemed like a holiday abroad when one was sick or poor, pine cones drooping on the trees like faded Christmas ornaments, echoes of music hanging like old rags upon a line.

She spotted his car in the bushes and saw him sitting

on the edge of the empty bandstand, a dark figure slumped over in the dawn, holding his head like a newly cracked vase.

"Thank you for coming, Mary," he said, nervously standing up. "Thank you." He was trying not to break, but the cracks were so apparent.

She could only nod, it was okay.

"I'm sorry, I mean about your mother, and the letters," his stutter gone, defeat, depression had robbed him of the tension which caused his nervous swallowing of words.

"I know," she said.

"I'm so lost, Mary, so lost." He looked around. "It's as though I left a trail of crumbs in the forest to assure my way home, and when I wasn't looking birds came and ate it up."

God, she wanted to weep.

He was like a giant magnet for her, her heart a nail, which made it worse.

"You made me happy, Mary."

What could she say?

"I couldn't hang on to happiness. I was hanging on a ledge and they pulled at me."

"I took off the ring," she said.

"What did you do with it?" he asked.

"Does someone want to know?" she asked.

Silence.

"I know," she said. "Peregrine wants to know." She opened her purse and took out his Death Poem, unopened. Hers had been in the trunk in their apartment, now Exhibit 507b in Court.

Their hands touched as he took the letter.

He moved closer to her.

"I haven't seen my family."

Was this for pity? To show how lonely his life was?

"I'm so alone. I have no friends. Please be my friend?" he asked.

"I can't," she said, "at least not now."

A ray of hope? He thought of ransom, offering money to buy back something that was really yours.

"Don't try to understand it, Mary," he said. "People aren't meant to be understood. They are not street signs or textbooks or songs that can be memorized. We can't understand life. We're not that kind, you and I."

"I'm not sure I understand things either," she said. "But I'm not going to do anything until I do, from now on."

"Touch me, Mary, my head is hot. I think I have a fever."

She didn't believe she did it, but she touched his head.

He lunged at her.

"Don't," she said.

"I can't forget you."

"Don't," she said again.

"We're married," he said.

Could she forgive him if she were white? Not being all white, lily white, Ivory soap white, the white that makes water ice and steel white-hot, Edison filament white, she still knew the answer—no, she would not forgive him, no matter what the outcome of the trial was.

"We were married, but you wrecked it," she said. "Not surgery or psychoanalysis or even amnesia would help. It was God's work. And it was undone."

"It wasn't God's work, Mary, it was us. We willed it."

"I unwill it then."

She ran. She had to.

Chapter 24

LEE RICHARDS THOMAS OPENED his seven-hour summary. He argued that Wyck wasn't stupid—he'd edited the paper at his school in Arizona, he'd passed his driver's test. He wrote hundreds of letters in which his command of erotic language rivaled that of Henry Miller. "Brain-tied youth! No. He was out for a good time. That is all. And he has had a fine time and gotten himself in a jam, and now he asks the senior member of the bar of Westchester County to get him out of it and crush what is left of this girl. He is through with his animalism and he will throw her aside and find some other form of amusement.

"Mr. Wells is trying to show you that he is an innocent boy—let's look at this innocent youth. It is his first experience. He carefully leaves Mary outside a strange hotel in New York City, takes the bags in, registers Mr. and Mrs. James Smith, Rye, New York. Let me ask you something from your understanding of human nature. Don't you think that if this were the first time, this stammering, brain-tied, nervous man would have been shaky? Why, I cannot conceive of anything that would require more boldness on the first occasion. Yet look at his handwriting on the register. Firm and natural. No signs of tremor or nervousness there. Compare it with his unsteady handwriting in the bill of particulars. Now if you gentlemen don't think he should have been scared to death and nervous as Sam Hill, then forget all this. But if you agree with me that he must have been a bold chap to do it, then think about it when you consider the question of who was the leader here.

"And, poor sweet innocent fellow. He knew about those rubber affairs, didn't he? We forced that admission out of him, didn't we? Right here.

"Innocence abroad? Well, he says he stayed at the hotel and went home only to have dinner with his father on Christmas night. Is that not proof of cold deception?

"And deception, gentlemen, is the 'gravamen' of this action. 'Gravamen,' if you are not familiar with that term, means the part of the charge that has the most weight. This man has charged deception against this girl and sat on that witness stand under cross-examination and said he never deceived anyone connected with the James family. Yet when he took that girl down to the Hotel Marie Antoinette, he was embarked on an enterprise of deceiving Mrs. James. He was embarked on an enterprise of deceiving his own father. If he would embark upon an enterprise of deception with them—do you think for one minute he would hesitate to deceive you twelve men to win this law suit?

"He does not come before you with clean hands. He comes before you with filthy ones. There is a well-recognized principle that one seeking justice and equity should walk into the courtroom with clean hands.

"There is another well-recognized principle in the courtroom and that is the principle of General Probability. All of your acts in life, or a great many of them, depend upon what you think is probable. It is a strong thing.

"If, for instance, a Chinaman came to you with a pigtail hanging down his back and said, 'I am an Englishman,' he would not defraud you because you could tell what he was by looking at him. That, ladies and gentlemen, is what happened in this case. It is surely probable that Edward Hanover could have known his wife's color, if he had wanted to.

"The most important question we have asked in this case is: Before Edward Hanover was married, did he know that his wife had colored blood? If he did, he is through, absolutely through in this case. Now, this is not said to hurt you, Mary, but gentlemen, you saw her body. Who could be fooled by her? You met her father. No disgrace to you, Mr. James, but who could think otherwise than that Mr. James had colored blood coursing through his veins?

"I expected an amendment to the complaint almost any time that Wyck Hanover was color-blind or totally blind. But they haven't gone that far. He isn't blind. Go into your jury room, and, in the face of what you saw here, say that it was at all probable that he believed he was marrying into a pure white family. Ah, he knew that she was colored, he knew it and he liked it until the family intervened. I repeat, he knew it and he liked it until some unforeseen power to protect the family name got back of him, and here he is and he must go through with it.

"There is just one question in this case, surrounded by all this testimony. Did she tell him that she was white, and did he believe it? Don't go out into your jury room and say, 'Here, we won't tie this young man up with a woman of colored blood.' You are not being asked that question. Remember that. And remember when you retire to your jury room that what has happened in this courtroom has destroyed any possibility of their ever living together again.

"Now, as I close, let me warn you. There is only one way, on the basis of this evidence, that Wells can win this case, and I tell you that he wants to win it badly, and I tell you that his attack on Mrs. James is a demonstration of that fact. If he can put your heart in place of your brain by oratory, maybe he can win. I fear his eloquence most of all."

His eyes filled with tears as he begged the jury to be fair. "You alone stand between this young girl and ruin. If this marriage is annuled, Mary will not be able to collect money. She will walk out of this courtroom shunned by the white race for being colored and shunned by the colored race for having hid the fact of it. God, what a life! And the Hanovers brought it about. They have torn the James home down over their heads. They have thrown this girl into the sewer and the slime, and she has only one thing left—her reputation for honesty, her clean reputation, her innocence. She is not a defrauder. Are you, on this paltry evidence, going to accuse her of that? Or are you at last going to say to this bunch, you have ruined this whole family, but we will give her something. We will turn her loose, whether she is black, white, or colored, and say that it is a damnable outrage for this man to charge her with fraud."

▪

Wells, persuasive, judicial, and oratorical by turn, showed Wyck Hanover as so enslaved and emotionally unbalanced that he could not tell black from white. "When he was eighteen she was in her twenty-third year. Women of her race mature quickly and are often mothers at fifteen. I claim that at eighteen, with his physical inferiorities and his backwardness, he possessed the intelligence of a boy of fourteen.

"He was putty in the hands of this Negro seductress. This nonvirgin who lied about her age, her race, her intention to marry him, and even went so far as to lie about her race on the marriage license. She denied her race to the representative of the court and to the press. That denial is what put Edward Wyck Hanover to the expense of sending twice across the seas into Old England to make investigations. That money might have been given to a hospital to provide solace and treatment for our poor sick. But it was wasted here, when Thomas rose at the opening of this trial and made this girl admit her color.

"Thomas says the issue of race has been 'eliminated.' But it has not. It is the lifeblood of this case. The issue of race was confessed. When Mary Hanover's race was proven by indisputable evidence, then my learned opponent folded his arms and said, 'I surrender.' Do not mistake the word. The issue is not eliminated. It is confessed.

"There is no wonder in my mind why this distinguished counsel did not subject the lady to my cross-examination. Hers was perjury plain and simple. Here was a web that has been spun by evil women, lying females since the biblical days of Eve, Bathsheba, since Samson and Delilah."

"Did they annul that marriage?" Thomas blurted out.

"This boy was easy victim to the Jameses' evil," Wells continued, ignoring Thomas's interruption. "Had his own mother lived, it is my firm belief that this case would never be in court. Look here at the malignity of a mixed marriage, the James family, what a pitiable sight. This woman marries a mulatto. There is no race prejudice in England among people in her class, but she found it when she came here. They work hard, save their money, buy land and houses. But with vaulting prosperity, vaulting ambition came to the mother's heart. There came the ambition to marry her daughters to white men. They attended a church with white people and a white Sunday School. Three daughters went out on the sidewalks and got white men and brought them into the house. The mother never questioned who they were. Or where they went. And this girl, Faye, who picked up this young man, got his ring on her finger the second night after she met him. And Mary led this poor inexperienced boy, this virgin, to bestial and unnatural acts two months after she met him. He did not know better. She led him to it.

"Your verdict, gentlemen, shall answer once more that ancient question put in the Holy Writ: 'Can the Ethiopian change his skin?' This mother, from her own ambition, entered upon that question. Your verdict must be in the negative—'No, it cannot be done.'

"Look at Mary, she has the same features that the father has. Long face. Aquiline nose. The other features of the Caucasian. The father's lips are as thin as my lips. You did not need to see her body. Her appearance would not condemn her to be of colored blood. Not at all. This young man is not to be blamed because he did not deduce that she was of colored blood.

"They went to the Hotel Marie Antoinette. Nobody thought she was a colored woman. This young man would not have been allowed there at all with a colored woman. All the men mentioned by Mary in her letters were white men, but they did not identify her as a colored girl. Mr. and Mrs. Rice wanted to break into society; well, that is no crime, but she took Mary to be white and went to a restaurant with her, and no one there thought she was a colored girl. A public official performing under his oath the duty of issuing a marriage license put her down as white. You have Mr. Claybourne, her first lawyer, a city judge of the city of New Rochelle, who accepted her affidavit as true. He must have seen her. He was not in love with her. And Mr. Thomas himself did not file this affidavit as to her color until it was proven way beyond anybody's doubt.

"How are you going to blame Edward Wyck Hanover, who was befuddled by her, for taking her as white when all these unbefuddled, independent witnesses took her for white?

"And Wyck himself has given you the best evidence that he believed she was white—because he married her in honorable marriage. And mind you, he was not drunk when he did it. He was not in the heat of passion. He was not tricked into it at the moment. He acted with such intelligence as he had.

"What is more, why did he leave her? He knew she was poor when he married her. He knew her social position when he married her. He had practically lived at the lowly James house. He knew his father was opposed. He loved her. He was loyal to her. He withstood the exposure in the newspapers. But then, in the end, he left her.

"What made him change his mind? It was but one fact. That she was of colored blood. When the issue was framed and joined and presented to him, he drew the line there. He was ready to go with her before the world as his wedded wife. He was ready to face the Four Hundred in the city, to stand against society side by side with the daughter of the Jameses, but when it was proven unto him by the presence and production of these birth certificates that she was of colored blood, then the change came in him.

"Gentlemen, do not chain my client to this mulatto. You might as well bury this young man six feet deep in the soil of an old churchyard where early American ancestors sleep. There is not a father among you, and I have hoped that this jury box would be filled with fathers, who would not rather see his son in a casket than with this young woman. With the buoyancy of her race, she will regain her spirits.

"You can have no hesitation about giving this young man freedom from this horrible, unnatural, absurd union. I have argued in court for three men whose very lives were in the balance of a verdict. I consider this case a fourth. It is a matter of the life and death of this young man.

"I pray you grant him deliverance, swift and true."

▪

It was one o'clock in the morning. The jury had been locked up for twelve hours. Down the corridor Thomas could hear their impassioned wrangling. He sat there, the moon littering the night with superstitions.

Mary was stretched out on the bench across from him in semisleep, her body like a sand dune, lunar ribbons in her hair. She was indeed a woman who could change the blood pressure of a man, make his heartbeat different and his mind go dull.

He remembered once asking her, "Do you think you'll ever fall in love again?"

"No," she said, very final.

"Are you sure?" he asked.

"Yes," she said. "A love like ours was a million-dollar gift. Once it's spent, it's gone. It was like a natural resource, a gold vein or oil underground. It's all mined out of me. Used up. There are only so many diamonds lying on a field."

"But if you win, Mary, you'll be rich. You can travel. You'll meet lots of people," he said.

"Lots of people will be meeting me, but I'll be all played out. De-jeweled. It's gone, Mr. Thomas. I have to think of something new besides loving and wifing and being a good mother to kids, because I don't think I'll ever have any."

Someone should sneak out there and throw more diamonds, he thought. If only one had diamonds.

He listened to the murmur of voices coming from the jury room. The law was like a window. He reviewed the case, seeing it as the jury did. Thomas had presented the view looking out one side. Wells the view looking from the other. Which side would the jury see the clearer, take for real?

If he lost, he would instantly appeal. He planned his moves.

▪

CLARENCE E. PAYNE, THE jury foreman, his clothes wrinkled and his mind askew, would have liked to make a speech, give an explanation, but he had been cautioned by the judge only to read the verdict, in a voice loud and clear. He stood to answer the questions charged to the jury by the court.

"One: At the time of the marriage between the plaintiff and the defendant, was the defendant colored and of colored blood? Yes.

"Two: Did the defendant, before the marriage, conceal from the plaintiff the fact that she was of colored blood? No.

"Three: Did the defendant, before the marriage, represent to the plaintiff that she was not of colored blood? No.

"Four: Did the defendant practice said concealment or make said representation with the intent thereby to induce the plaintiff to marry her? No."

And besides, the foreman said in an interview later, Mr. Hanover would have married her no matter what. His fervid letters attested to that point.

"It was fraud we were deciding," added the juror. "Race

prejudice was not an issue. If we had voted with our hearts, the results might have been different."

▪

MARY WAS LEAVING WHITE Plains and the courthouse, for good. At the crowded railroad station, where she was waiting for the train to take her home, there was a big victory celebration. She was hoisted up by redcaps (some carrying banners, for this was the year of A. Philip Randolph's movement for the Brotherhood of Sleeping Car Porters and Maids). A loud and brassy jazz band was playing the Cakewalk, and people cheered and wished her well. The Ku Klux Klan hung on the fringes of the group.

The cause of love had been avenged. Flappers asked Mary for autographs. They did not understand that love does not want retribution. Love only wants more love.

Alma Sioux Mayberry of KBAY, Los Angeles, had never in her career of following celebrity romances felt so helpless, nonobjective, caught within a trial. She would go home and cry until her socks were wet. It all escaped her, this waste of beauty, waste of love, and she squinted at Mary like a stargazer on a cloudy night.

A colleague of Alma Sioux's pushed his way toward Mary and asked her, "Do you still love him?"

"Well," she said, "I do and I don't." It was all over and a great feeling of loneliness had just begun. She had seen him daily in court and now she was to see him no more. Say goodbye, Mary, be brave and say goodbye, she thought. "It's awfully sad," she said.

"Do you think any good has come out of this trial?" someone asked.

"I've gained many friends as a result of it. I've gotten closer to my family, and I want to thank them for staying with me all this time," said Mary.

Alma Sioux wanted to touch Mary and reached over to her. Mary took her hand. "It was such a beautiful love," said Alma, "I could tell."

"There are some things that even love cannot forgive," said Mary.

"Are you happy that you won?" asked a French reporter.

"I couldn't win. There was no happy ending here." It would close forever on untied bows and rainbows without light and water stains on silk and crystal glasses chipped, her love, the lyrics of a song.

"Would you ever go back to him?" asked someone.

"No. No," she said. Tears welled up like mountains in her throat, her promise not to cry outdistanced, you're not a baby, Mary, you're not a baby anymore.

"It is felt that you two had an unusually fine and beautiful affair," said a reporter.

Mary, suddenly reverting back to the grammar of her letters, answered softly, "Yes, yes, it were."

▪

Elizabeth James went home to plant her winter garden—circumpolar plants and frore roses and snow buttercups and glacier lilies and shrubs with fuzz-covered leaves to shield them from winter winds. Long days had turned to short days, the annuals had died, the perennials surviving only in their seeds. She would wrap her bulbs and mulch the earth, protect the plants that could survive a frost with tents of paper, glass panes mounted on wire frames. She would treat her daughter as part of her winter garden, waiting carefully for better days, expecting no bloom, the season in her daughter's life had all too quickly changed.

▪

"I WAS A CHILD of love, a girl of vanity, and I will not age with hate," Mary said in the last interview she gave the press. And she didn't. There were changes in her life, though. She still liked the tabloids and chapter plays at the movies, but they were no longer storybook tales, images in a parade marching outside and past her. Now she was part of that parade, cared deeply about heroines in danger, and victims of crimes, and soldiers returning from wars.

She would recover. She would heal.

She had once read a fairy tale about a princess who was certain that she would live forever with a sorrow that would never cease. The king and queen argued with her—beauty or pleasure or laughter would break her sorrow. They called upon wizards and wise men, artists and clowns, but nothing could dispel her sadness. Finally, everyone agreed with the young girl that the sorrow was hers for the rest of her life. But when they told her that, the princess began to be happy. The sorrow fled.

If she told herself that she had been libeled, shamed, unsexed, scarred, hurt beyond repair, maybe something inside her would lift as it had for the princess. Didn't that jazz music the band was playing send her spirits zooming? Hadn't her parents showed her love could last and feelings needn't change? And now she would have money and it could buy her dresses and she could travel and see the world. Maybe people were better, somewhere else.

She would let go her sadness (maybe not today, maybe not until springtime), but she would be able to break the spell that this taking away of love had cast.

Brown? Tan? No, she was Mary. Smarter, yes. Worldly now. She would look inside things, think more about what people said. She would protect herself forever from the bare-boned frame of love. But she was Mary still.

▪

As FOR WYCK, HE shut himself off, not even watching the parade around him, spending days in a room with the shutters drawn, his meals brought up on trays.

Sadness was all he remembered, all he saw in place of that horizon of love at the Rainbow Box. The crowded floor of moving dancers was replaced by stilled, unpeopled rooms. He barely noticed the rented suite in which he lived. A game of cards with an acquaintance, a visit to a store for clothes—those were his only outings.

He never saw his family. There had been no confrontation. Father had released him from his old life without providing him a new one. His bodyguards watched, but there was little to see. His energies now gone, he had no wherewithal to find new friends, let alone new love.

He drifted not in a sea of dancers but in spilt milk, tears stored up, feelings curdled from old heat. He drifted until the moisture got into his lungs. Too much dampness, perhaps one day the weather added to it all, and he got pneumonia. And he could not say he was unhappy when he drifted out of a life he knew as pain.

Mary sent a simple group of everlasting buds, not allowed to flower, not allowed to flourish, not allowed to age.

▪

MARY JAMES HANOVER SUED for divorce and won a quarter-million-dollar settlement, which enabled her to travel, lecture, and do the Charleston with the best of them. And she never called herself a little Spanish kid again.